Dan Ferguson

D0008280

Flush Production

Flush
Production

THE EPIC OF OIL IN
THE GULF-SOUTHWEST

By GERALD FORBES

UNIVERSITY OF OKLAHOMA PRESS

NORMAN   1942

To My Wife

◇◇◇◇◇◇◇◇ ACKNOWLEDGMENT ◇◇◇◇◇◇◇◇

POSSIBLY the most delightful aspect of the research for and writing of this manuscript has been the pleasure of receiving the assistance of others. I am especially indebted to President Joseph A. Brandt, of the University of Oklahoma, for suggesting the subject of this study, and to my wife, Jean West Forbes, for verifying the references and statements.

Among other persons whose suggestions have been of value are: Mr. Robert H. Dott and Mr. J. O. Beach, of the Oklahoma Geological Survey; Dr. J. Huner, Jr., of the Louisiana Geological Survey; Mr. Grady Triplett, of *The Refiner and Natural Gasoline Manufacturer;* Professor V. G. Sleight, of the University of Arkansas; Mr. Charles W. Eliot, chairman of the National Resources Planning Board; Mr. Neil Williams and Mr. William T. Ziegenhaine, of *The Oil and Gas Journal;* President C. E. Needham, of the New Mexico School of Mines; Professor R. L. Biesele and Professor George Ward Stocking, of the University of Texas; Mr. James H. Gardner, of the Gardner Petroleum Corporation; Mr. C. V. Millikan, of the Amerada Petroleum Corporation; Professor Fred A. Shannon, of the University of Illinois; Mr. O. W. Meyers, of the Sinclair Prairie Oil Company; Mr. Nelson K. Moody, of the Sinclair Prairie Oil Marketing Company; Dr. Norman D. FitzGerald, of the Chase National Bank; Mr. Wallace Pratt, of the Standard Oil Company of New Jersey; Professor Paul H. Giddens, of Allegheny College; Mr. Boyce House, of Fort Worth, Texas; Mr. K. C. Sclater, of *The Petroleum Engineer*. The staff of the University of Oklahoma Press, too, has been especially helpful.

Any errors in interpretation, judgment, or fact are my responsibility.

GERALD FORBES

Tahlequah, Oklahoma
July 15, 1942

vii

CONTENTS

Flush Production

Spudding In*

IN the geologically recent past, seas ebbed and flowed
over the region that now constitutes the oil-producing
Gulf-Southwest. Sand and mud, derived from the de-
struction of rocks on the adjacent continent, were washed
into the sea by rivers. Plant and animal life settled on the
bottom and helped to fill the resulting sedimentary domain.
As time elapsed and petroleum was formed, it was caught
in three types of traps that came into being. There were
folds in the layers of stone in which petroleum accumulated. Cracks or faults in the hard formations also caught
and held the liquid minerals. Huge cones of salt created the
third type of trap when they were thrust upward through
the layers of the earth to make crevasses that also might
be filled with petroleum. The two great oil-bearing regions
of the world are those surrounding the Gulf of Mexico–
Caribbean Sea and the Mediterranean Sea. In the southwestern part of the United States there are sedimentary
areas estimated to be nearly ten miles in thickness, although drilling tools have not been devised to explore such
depths for petroleum. Some geologists, however, believe
that more oil will be discovered there in the future than
has been produced in the past.

Early in the nineteenth century, the pioneers and Indians of the Southwest found and used the petroleum of

*In the phraseology of the oil industry, the actual start in drilling a well
is referred to as "spudding in."

3

numerous seepages. Before the Civil War, the crude "rock oil" was sold in bottles as a tonic. As its medicinal desirability declined, two new and important uses for petroleum, illumination and lubrication, developed. Seepages of petroleum, varying from gas to asphalt, were discovered throughout the states of the Gulf-Southwest. By 1900 the great oil industry had become a young giant in the Appalachian region and was stretching strong arms in the Gulf-Southwest. Paralleling the early events in the oil industry was the beginning of the internal-combustion engine and automotive manufacturing. By 1940 the manufacture of motor vehicles was the largest industry in the United States, while refining of petroleum ranked fourth. About three-fourths of the petroleum of the United States was produced from wells in the six states of Kansas, Oklahoma, Texas, Arkansas, Louisiana, and New Mexico, which are hereinafter referred to as southwestern.

One-third of the energy now consumed in the United States is derived from petroleum. The petroleum industry has permitted the manufacture and use of about thirty million motor vehicles, which in turn have caused the construction of thousands of miles of paved roads throughout the country. Aircraft, which span the continent in a few hours, consume more than one hundred million gallons of fuel yearly. Thousands of locomotives and ships depend on the petroleum industry for power. High-speed machines require dependable lubricants which the oil industry supplies.

This industry has brought more than eight billions of dollars in new wealth to the Gulf-Southwest, where it has been distributed among all classes, from laborers to professional men. Every division of the government, from school districts upward, has collected taxes from the oil industry. In some of the states this revenue has been the chief source of income, while throughout the United States the tax collected from petroleum and its products approached $1,500,000,000 in 1940. In passing through the processes of producing, manufacturing, and marketing, a barrel of petroleum yields more than one dollar in taxes. Especial attention has been focused on the industry by the mechanized warfare being waged in so many parts of the world. Petroleum has become an imperative factor in the international civil, political, industrial, and military life.

It has been the intention in this book to present in readable length the vigorous growth in the Gulf-Southwest of this internationally vital industry. The limitations may have caused inadequate treatment in places, for many interesting details were omitted. The desire has been to follow the most significant movements and yet to present an understanding background for the many problems of this important element in American life. The first four chapters relate the chronological development, thus permitting definite phases to be treated separately. The important factors to which later chapters have been devoted include: scientific changes, the activities of the speculator, the natural gas industry, transportation, the social adjustments, legal aspects, governmental control, and oil-field lore.

Obviously, in a work of this sort, which covers such an enormous range, not merely geographically but in time and in fact, an effort to give citations would greatly overburden the text. Special attention must be called, therefore, to the comprehensive bibliography offered, which sustains the narrative of the study.

From Seepage
to Spindletop

A BOUT eighty years elapsed between the drilling of the first oil producer and the completion in 1901 of the Spindletop gusher, the well popularly credited with having been the greatest of all time. During the second fifty years of the nineteenth century, oil and natural gas were discovered in commercial quantities in four of the southwestern states—Kansas, Oklahoma, Texas, and Louisiana. In those years, the roots of the young petroleum industry achieved a sturdy growth in the region, an area that was destined to dominate the oil business of the United States.

It was on the Bermuda Plantation, near the Cane River, Natchitoches Parish, Louisiana, between 1821 and 1825, that slave labor drilled a deep well for water and found a little gas. The well, bored with a modified rotary tool made by the plantation blacksmith, was reported to have struck oil four times. A square cypress casing was fitted into the hole.[1] As early as 1839, along the Calcasieu River near Lake Charles, Louisiana, oil was sometimes collected and used.

Numerous stories of the existence of oil and gas seepages followed those early records of petroleum. Indians in Texas and the Indian Territory bathed for their health

[1] It is likely that the significance of the oil in the Bermuda well has been exaggerated.—Grady Triplett, "History of North Louisiana," *The Oil Weekly*, Vol. LXXXIX, No. 3 (March 28, 1938), 92.

in the oil-coated springs. Ranchmen, pioneer farmers, and freighters observed greasy water in springs and well buckets. There were occasions when the oil was skimmed off and used to lubricate the heavy wagons. By the middle of the century there were many records of surface indications of petroleum throughout the Southwest. Between 1852 and 1870 geologists in Kansas and Texas investigated the Carboniferous, Permian, Cretaceous, and Tertiary formations. The first Kansas State Geological Survey was authorized in 1864, and two years later the first report was made; but the deposits of coal attracted more attention than did the possibility of producing petroleum.

It was in 1859 that a driller named Jack Graham predicted that oil would be found in Texas on a line between Nacogdoches and the Sabine River. Graham based his prophecy on the discoveries he made at a well which he had dug with a spring pole in Angelina County. An oil seepage near Saratoga, Texas, used as a hog wallow, resulted in another spring-pole drilling enterprise; but one hundred feet was as deep as the hand-powered machinery would drill, so the well was abandoned. Near an oil spring not far from the town of Nacogdoches a well one hundred feet deep produced a little oil before the Civil War. During the war nothing further was done, but leasing became active in 1865, and in 1866 the search for oil was extended to Harris, Hardin, Liberty, Polk, Tyler, Jefferson, Clay, Young, Cooke, Angelina, Fannin, Bexar, and McLennan counties. By the use of a divining rod, B. T. Kavanaugh, a colorful doctor of medicine and divinity, became convinced that oil was to be found in northern Texas and in the Indian Territory. He failed to follow his clues, but in 1866 he leased the land near Beaumont that later was to be a part of the spectacular Spindletop Pool. Lynis T. Barrett returned in 1866 to the leases he had acquired near

Nacogdoches before the war and drilled a well 106 feet deep which passed through a small amount of oil, gas, and water.

Paralleling the developments in Texas was a series of events in Kansas, for near Paola an asphalt seepage led to an effort to produce petroleum in 1858. Two other insignificant wells were drilled there in 1860–61, and to take advantage of the increased depth a third hole was sunk in the bottom of a water well. The prospecting company, which had leased thirty thousand acres of Miami County land, drilled only futile wells, but it was handicapped by limited resources and the fact that its equipment would make a hole only one hundred feet deep. The Civil War interfered with this enterprise also, for two members of the firm joined the Confederate Army and left Kansas; and Quantrell's raid on Lawrence in 1863 ruined several of the interested men. After the Civil War more drilling was undertaken in Wyandotte County, but money for prospecting was difficult to raise, and only a little oil and gas were found. The Kansas State Geologist studied Miami County and made a favorable report, which caused the organization of several companies. The indifference of the drillers and the scarcity of funds, however, resulted in the failure of these organizations. The little petroleum that was found was dark and thick, but was considered more desirable than the thin, amber-colored varieties. The presence of gas in abundance was disclosed by these early Kansas wells.

During the decade of the seventies the development of the oil industry in the southwestern states was negligible. At Shreveport, Louisiana, gas was struck by drillers who were seeking water for an ice plant. The gas was used to light the ice plant and as fuel for drilling other wells. In several Kansas localities companies were organized to seek petroleum, and near Paola some gas-producing wells were

drilled. Paola was looked on as the center of the new oil
and gas industry. Gas was piped there for use as fuel in
1873. It was during this decade that the pipe of a farmer
in Washington County, Texas, ignited the gas that came
from a well drilled with a hand auger for water.[2]

The Kansas oil industry received an impetus in 1881
from which it did not recede, when John J. Werner, a
former driller in Pennsylvania, and H. J. Foote, of Olathe,
Kansas, agreed to enter the petroleum industry. They
hired a livery rig at Baxter Springs and spent several days
among the citizens of the Indian Territory, with some of
whose chiefs they signed leases. Later they learned that
the Department of the Interior had supervisory authority
over the Indian lands, so they abandoned the exploration
of the territory. They went to Paola, where they organized
the Kansas Oil, Gas and Mining Company and leased a
farm which contained a so-called "tar spring." Drilling
tools were purchased at Bradford, Pennsylvania, for twelve
hundred dollars, and in 1882 gas was found at a depth of
305 feet. Continued drilling only produced more gas. The
only revenue from the first well came from the sale of
drinks at a dance hall where the gas was used for lighting.
Such small quantities of oil as were accumulated at the
gas wells were sold readily as lubricants at three to five
dollars a barrel.

It had been established definitely that petroleum existed
in Wyandotte, Cherokee, Brown, Atchison, Riley, and
Leavenworth counties in Kansas; but in no case was the
amount believed to be marketable. No greater was the

[2] In 1876 the Texas Legislature first considered setting aside land for the
support of the state university. The original plan would have given the
University of Texas one million acres in East Texas, an area later to prove
rich with oil. The final allotment of lands in West Texas, however, also contained a great store of petroleum.

reward for the searchers to the south and west, where the belief was prevalent that petroleum existed only in small quantities. Near Lake Charles, Louisiana, it was recorded that a noncommercial amount of oil was present in Calcasieu Parish. The New Mexico Bitumen and Oil Company attempted to drill a well on the Navajo Reservation, but the Indians drove the workmen away. Despite the general attention that the search for petroleum had attracted, coal still was considered more valuable and usable. Petroleum was valued for its kerosene, which was used chiefly in lighting, while coal was more desired for heating. At Independence, Kansas, a shaft was sunk in the search for coal. At twelve hundred feet it produced gas and oil in such quantities that it was ignited by the fire in the near-by boiler, and all the wood in the vicinity was burned. The gas and oil were not considered valuable enough to commercialize, and the project was abandoned in 1884. Two years later the city of Independence granted a franchise for serving the town with artificial gas, but the company failed for want of customers. It was not until 1887 that the success of the natural gas industry at Paola caused the effort to supply Independence with gas to be revived.

Veterans in the production of petroleum in Pennsylvania contributed to setting ambitious plans on foot for the development of the oil near Nacogdoches, Texas, in 1886. The Petroleum Prospecting Company, capitalized at one hundred thousand dollars, completed its first well at seventy feet, and the initial flow was estimated at about three hundred barrels a day. Experienced men came from Pennsylvania to develop the pool, and hundreds of leases on the surrounding land were signed. One man assembled twenty-three leases on a total of 4,441 acres. Several companies were organized to participate in the development. By 1890 the Petroleum Prospecting Company had twenty producers and was moving its oil fourteen miles by a pipe line to Nacogdoches. The Lubricating Oil Company built a crude refinery on its holdings, and by evaporating the lighter parts of the oil it prepared a lubricant for the market. All the operators, however, realized that the pool was small, and soon it was abandoned.

Simultaneously with the developments in Kansas and Texas there was a movement among the Cherokees and Choctaws to develop the suspected petroleum resources in those two nations. In 1884 the two tribal governments approved the organization of Indian companies that were to induce oil firms to enter the Indian Territory. Hiram W. Fawcett, formerly of Pennsylvania, acquired monopolistic leases on tribal lands and drilled two unsuccessful wells near the present cities of Atoka and Tahlequah, Oklahoma, where there were surface indications of oil. These dry wells were followed by one that was drilled near Eufaula, in the Creek Nation, where gas was reported to have been found at three different depths. It was near the end of the 1880's that an old man named Palmer drilled a well by hand in the Chickasaw Nation. He reached a depth of about 425 feet and black crude oil—the same that later, on this very spot, was to make the Healdton Pool famous—flowed from the top of the hole. For years the oil from Palmer's well was used by residents of the neighborhood for lubricating.

The first commercial oil well in present-day Oklahoma was drilled by horsepower in 1889 near Chelsea, Cherokee Nation, by a contractor who received eighty cents a foot. Oil was encountered at a depth of less than two hundred feet. A pump was installed and the crude petroleum was taken in five-gallon cans to Independence, Kansas, where it was sold to grease the tracks of the horse-drawn streetcars. Kansas definitely became an oil-producing state in

1889, when several wells in a new area near Paola yielded a total of five hundred barrels, which was sold for about five dollars a barrel. Ten men were employed by the industry, and about $160,000 had been invested. Leases in the state totaled more than four thousand acres, and that year oil was discovered at Fort Scott, Wyandotte, and Coffeyville. In Texas, meanwhile, George Dulnig, a ranchman living near San Antonio, drilled two wells that produced about four barrels of oil a month. He sold it to the neighbors at twenty cents a gallon.

The final decade of the century was one with a great deal of successful activity among the prospectors, many of whom had come from Pennsylvania and were seeking petroleum in the Southwest. A heavy lubricating oil from a spring in Bernalillo County, New Mexico, was sold locally for ten dollars a barrel. In Texas, where the work was done by cowboys, a total investment of $1,650 was recorded for the industry. More fruitful were the activities in Kansas, for one prospector interested the firm of J. M. Guffey and John H. Galey, of Pittsburgh, Pennsylvania, in seeking oil near Neodesha. The value of the petroleum produced in Kansas in 1891 was fixed at $9,800, and that year the state officials recognized the importance of the industry by enacting an oil and gas conservation law. The next year a well was started near Neodesha which in 1893 produced about a dozen barrels of oil a day and resulted ultimately in the construction of a refinery and the organization of a pipe-line company. By 1894 there were more than forty wells in the Neodesha district.

While the production of oil in Kansas was developing as rapidly as the marketing facilities permitted, men entered the Indian Territory to prospect there also. They felt that the Indian lands surely must contain oil as valuable as that found in Kansas, since the surface was so

13

similar. Several agreements were made with the different tribes, but only one of these blanket leases became the basis for active oil development. Widespread exploratory work was prevented by the consideration of the allotment of Indian lands. In 1894 Michael Cudahy, a meat packer of Omaha, Nebraska, drilled two wells on town lots in the village of Muskogee, Creek Nation. Oil was found, but the quantity did not invite further investment. This was followed by another drilling, across the Arkansas River from the little Creek hamlet of Tulsa. The oil found there was not significant, so again Cudahy moved his machinery. This time a well was drilled on the Caney River not far from the trading post of Jacob Bartles, which later was to become Bartlesville. In 1897 this fourth well also found a small amount of oil, but it was capped and remained closed for several years. It was a year earlier, in 1896, that Edwin B. Foster leased the entire Osage Reservation with the approval of the United States Department of the Interior. This was the only successful blanket lease of Indian land, and one of the provisions of the contract required that drilling for oil be started within a year. So in 1897 Foster completed a well on Osage land near the Kansas line, and again a small quantity of oil was discovered. Foster capped his well also, and it was not reopened until after the close of the century. In ten years petroleum had been discovered in six widely separated localities in the Indian and Oklahoma territories.[3]

At the same time that these discoveries were being made in the Indian country south of Kansas, Texas was joining

[3] By 1898, about twenty-seven wells had been drilled in the Indian Territory, most of them before 1896. The difficulty of perfecting a title to the tribally owned lands hindered the development of the oil industry, for the Department of the Interior permitted one person or company to control no more than 640 acres.

in the establishment of the oil industry. In 1894 the city officials of Corsicana discovered petroleum at a depth of 1,027 feet while drilling a municipal water well. Casing was placed in the hole and the well was deepened to a satisfactory vein of water. The oil rose to the surface around the casing, however, and attracted the attention of several citizens of the town. A local company was organized, and drilling for petroleum started, but most of the citizens continued to mind their gardens. The first well of the firm, the American Well and Prospecting Company, produced less than five barrels of oil a day, and while it was being drilled the careless spectators burned three derricks. The second well produced about twenty barrels; and by 1896 the pool was yielding nearly fifteen hundred barrels of petroleum daily. The drilling continued so that by 1897 the daily production at Corsicana was up to sixty-five thousand barrels. Since it had become increasingly important to find a commercial outlet for the oil, J. S. Cullinan, a young Pennsylvanian, was induced to visit Corsicana. He agreed to lay a pipe line, build storage tanks, develop a market, and purchase 150,000 barrels of crude oil at fifty cents a barrel. Cullinan arranged for financial assistance in the East, but a gloomy report from geologists caused the financiers to cancel the agreement. Then he gained the aid of officials of the Standard Oil Company. It was on Christmas Day, 1898, that the fires first were lighted under the stills of the refinery at Corsicana. That was the first permanent refinery to be constructed in Texas, although in February that year a short-lived plant with a capacity of one hundred barrels had been erected at Sour Lake on the Gulf Coast. About four hundred miles to the north, a five-hundred-barrel refinery had been in operation at Neodesha for a year.

When the century drew toward its close, petroleum had

been found in commercial quantities in Texas, in the Indian Territory, and in Kansas. Leading the Texas production was the Corsicana Pool, where one hundred wells were flowing and thirty were being pumped with a daily output of enough oil to support a refinery. The Corsicana development had brought the first eastern capital to the oil industry in Texas, and had resulted in the construction of the first permanent refinery in the state. The pool had been the laboratory for the perfection of a practical rotary drilling bit. It was here also that oil first was used for surfacing unpaved streets and that the first experiment in the use of oil as a fuel for locomotives was made. Just as the Neodesha Pool had caused the first oil conservation law in Kansas, so did the Texas Legislature respond to the Corsicana Pool. The pool also stimulated a great amount of exploratory drilling throughout the Southwest. Among the important explorations was one at Chanute, Kansas, where in 1899 I. N. Knapp drilled several successful wells from which he shipped oil to Omaha and Kansas City in 1900. In 1900 Kansas produced 74,714 barrels of petroleum valued at $69,142, and Texas produced 836,039 barrels valued at $871,996. A characteristic feature of this early development of the oil industry was the fact that only local interest was aroused by the production of oil or the finding of new pools. It is true that, in contrast to the times which followed, few dramatic or exciting events had occurred in those early years.

The spectacular drama of 1901 which marked the beginning of a new era in the southwestern oil industry really had its inception about 1893, when Captain Anthony F. Lucas, a mining engineer, began prospecting for oil in southern Louisiana. At that time Pattillo Higgins, a wildcat lease broker, had acquired leases on more than one thousand acres of land near Beaumont, Texas, and had organized the Gladys City Oil, Gas and Manufacturing Company. A contract was let to drill a well two thousand feet deep on Big Hill, or Sour Spring Mound, which was also known as Spindletop, about three miles from Beaumont. At about sixty feet gas was found; and when the hole was a little more than four hundred feet deep a gale blew the derrick down. The supply of wood for fuel could not be replenished because rain flooded the surrounding land. Sand filled the hole during the enforced shutdown, so work on the well was abandoned. The prospects at Spindletop did not attract Captain Lucas from the salt-dome region of Louisiana for six years. In 1899 he abandoned his enterprises in Louisiana and joined Higgins in seeking oil by drilling on the edge of Spindletop Hill, which had an area of approximately 125 acres and at its highest point was about forty feet above sea level.[4]

Lucas and Higgins, after exhausting their own funds, gained the assistance of the firm of Guffey and Galey. The financial aid of the Pittsburgh men was acquired only after Lucas had leases or options on twenty-seven thousand acres. Then it was agreed to drill three wells twelve hundred feet deep. Lucas started his second well on October 27, 1900. Circulating water was used to remove the cuttings, principally sand, from the hole; muddy water removed the sand more efficiently, so cows were driven into the pit to stir it. The drill passed through soft formations for more than one

[4] Captain Anthony F. Lucas was a son of the family of Luchich, born in Dalmatia in 1855. He was graduated from an Austrian engineering school, after which he became an officer in the Austrian navy. Discontented, he resigned his commission to emigrate to the United States, where he became a citizen. In 1885 he became a consultant in the salt and sulphur mines of Louisiana. C. W. Hayes, chief of the United States Geological Survey, and Calvin Paine, geologist for the Standard Oil Company, urged Lucas not to drill at Spindletop. "Now that we've got her, boys, how are we going to close her up?" shouted Lucas when the well blew in.

thousand feet. Then on January 11, 1901, a six-inch stream of oil and gas blew both the tools and casing out of the hole. At its peak the dark petroleum rose more than 160 feet into the air. Between 70,000 and 110,000 barrels of oil flowed from the wild well each of the nine days before it was controlled. It was estimated that this well alone produced one-sixth of the world's output of petroleum during 1901, and the surrounding countryside was saturated with oil that collected in the low places. At least 500,000 barrels of petroleum flowed on the ground. At once ninety guards were employed to watch the well night and day, while forty double teams were busy constructing earthen storage. Serious damage was caused, but the well was not burned, when a spark from a passing locomotive ignited the oil on the ground. In an effort to sell the petroleum the owners of the well communicated with the Standard Oil Company, and a group of officers of that firm visited Beaumont and inspected the discovery.

"Too big, too big," said the leader of the party as they left. "There's more oil here than the whole world will need for the next century—not for us!"

It was then that T. Mellon and Sons, bankers, of Pittsburgh, entered the Texas oil industry through the building of a pipe line twenty miles long to Port Arthur. Another rich man interested in the Texas oil industry at that time was John W. ("Bet-a-Million") Gates, who also financed a pipe line.

By July there were fourteen wells in the Spindletop Pool, and before the end of the year there were 138 producers; forty-six more were being drilled, while twenty-eight had been abandoned. There were steel storage tanks with a total capacity of 2,825,000 barrels, in addition to earthen reservoirs that held still more thousands. The railway loading racks would accommodate 161 tank cars at one time, and there were three small refineries. The total investment amounted to $3,951,085.

In December it was clear that the 138 wells atop the hill itself occupied the area of important production, and the surface of the pool never was more than three hundred acres. Some of the wells produced ten thousand to seventy thousand barrels daily, and a scramble for the valuable space developed. The top of the hill was divided into tracts as small as one square yard, and drillers were forced to borrow derrick space from their neighbors. Scaffolds were laid from derrick to derrick to provide for the escape of the workmen if the wells blew in or caught fire. Some of the plots, just large enough for one derrick, were sold for thousands of dollars. Some of the dry wells produced oil from neighboring holes that were poorly cased. There were 500 wells on five acres, and in eighteen months 750 wells were abandoned—a number that increased to 1,000 in four years. During the first year five million barrels of oil were marketed from Spindletop, at prices that varied from three to seventeen cents a barrel. In 1901, when Texas accounted for about one-fifth of the petroleum of the nation, it was believed that the Spindletop Pool might ultimately produce eighteen million barrels of oil.

This amazing pool attracted men from all parts of the United States and Canada, who signed leases and options on land for miles in every direction from Spindletop. The effect of the gusher on the oil industry was shown by the organization in the United States of 1,578 oil companies. The total capital stock authorized or issued was $669,083,000. In Texas alone 619 firms were formed with a total capitalization of $283,508,000; 122 of them found oil. Of all the companies springing out of the Spindletop hysteria, only three became permanently important. Millions of dollars worth of oil company stock, much of it

19

fraudulent and with entirely fictitious value, was sold, causing the pool to become known as "Swindletop."

Beaumont, where the streets were often deep in mud and the air was alive with mosquitoes, swarmed with humanity. Any space with a roof commanded a high rent, and many of the stock salesmen and so-called company officials occupied sidewalk space, which consisted of two chairs, a packing case, and an umbrella. The contrasting dissolute and respectable elements that later were to populate the southwestern oil boom towns were represented in the conglomerate mass of human beings attracted by Spindletop, where an oil well first flowed by natural pressure.

While the influence of Spindletop was felt throughout the United States, its most direct effect was the stimulation of exploratory drilling in Texas, Louisiana, and the Indian Territory. Wells were put down in sixteen counties of Texas, some of them many miles from Spindletop. Strenuous efforts to duplicate the Beaumont well were made in near-by Louisiana at the towns of Jennings, Welsh, Lake Charles, and Sulphur. In Acadia Parish, near Jennings, the men who had acquired the property of Captain Lucas when he left for Texas found petroleum. In 1902 a second well at Jennings, more than eighteen hundred feet deep, flowed over the top of the derrick.

Spindletop, the discovery pool of the coastal salt domes, marked the end of the age of kerosene and the beginning of the era of gasoline; for in the consumption of petroleum products the internal-combustion engine was to replace the lamp. The frantic expansion and growth of Beaumont developed the first boom in the six oil-producing states of the Gulf-Southwest. There had been no devil-may-care plunging and speculating at Corsicana or Neodesha, but after Beaumont many an oil town was nailed together in a few months. The Spindletop Pool caused many other salt

The Spindletop Well at Beaumont, Texas, with Captain Lucas, the discoverer, in buggy at left

*Early pumps for shallow strippers were built on the job
and operated by a central power system*

*Modern equipment for deep well pumping includes an
individual power plant*

domes to be explored for petroleum. The limited marketing and transporting facilities combined with the apparently unlimited amount of oil resulted in the sale of great quantities at a rate of a few cents a barrel. The first successful refinery of the Gulf Coast was erected at Port Arthur, and the Houston and Texas Central Railway began burning oil in its locomotives. Spindletop, generally known as the world's greatest oil well, was the beginning of the "modern" oil industry of the Gulf-Southwest. It is quite possible that since 1901 many wells have been greater producers than this one, but the consequences of the exciting Beaumont event tend to validate the early estimates of it.

Demands Spur Production

THE excitement surrounding the discovery and exploitation of several immense pools and hundreds of smaller oil-producing areas punctuated the first fifteen years of this century. The influence of the older Appalachian oil fields became strong in the Gulf-Southwest during this time, as experienced men in increasing numbers moved from Pennsylvania, West Virginia, Ohio, and other states. Many of the developments were supervised by men initiated at Bradford or Oil City, who brought the catalogues of Pennsylvania equipment houses in their bags. Thus the experience and the tools were transplanted to the newer region.

It was during this period that the automobile manufacturers created an enormous and steadily growing market for gasoline. When Spindletop roused the country, there were eight thousand motor cars and less than two hundred miles of paved highways in the United States. Some leaders of the busy automobile industry feared that the manufacture of gasoline would fail to keep pace with their mounting output. As the demand for gasoline grew, dramatic stories of suddenly gained wealth created a favorable popular attitude from which salesmen of speculative oil stock reaped a harvest of millions of dollars in a far-flung campaign for investors and "suckers." Companies were formed right and left, and stock, often with doubtful value, was sold throughout the United States, while exploratory wells in the six states of the Gulf-Southwest were watched eagerly by potential investors.

The most productive of the six southwestern states was Oklahoma, which for half of this period was known officially as the Oklahoma Territory and the Indian Territory. Since most of the exploration was done on the newly allotted lands of the Indians, the records are both vague and complicated in many cases. By 1900, however, more than twenty wells appear to have been drilled in northeastern Oklahoma in the Cherokee and Creek nations, as well as several in the Osage Nation. Shallow pools around Chelsea, Alluwe, and Coody's Bluff were producing oil in marketable quantities. Oklahoma was the source of about ten thousand barrels of petroleum in 1901, when prospectors wandered over the eastern and southern sections of the future state.

CHRONOLOGICAL TABLE
OF OKLAHOMA OIL POOLS, 1901–15

Pool	Year Discovered	County and Region
Red Fork	1901	Creek, northeast
Glenn	1905	Creek, northeast
Cushing	1912	Creek, northeast
Healdton	1913	Carter, south
Blackwell	1914	Kay, north central

It was in June, 1901, at Red Fork, Indian Territory, that a boom occurred with as little foundation as any in the history of the oil industry. The Creek Nation had leased about five hundred thousand acres of land to John S. Wick, a former Pennsylvania driller. Wick interested Jesse A. Heydrick, also of Pennsylvania, and a company was formed to explore for oil. Heydrick selected the location for the well and employed a driller from Missouri. Strict secrecy surrounded all the operations. The plan was to drill at least twelve hundred feet.

Late one night Wick visited the well and saw a spray of oily mud and gas blow from the casing when the drill penetrated a gas pocket at about 540 feet. He forgot his promise of secrecy and quickly sent a telegram to the driller, who was in Joplin, that oil was spouting over the top of the derrick. The announcement, with dramatic exaggeration, spread excitement throughout the Indian and Oklahoma territories.[1] Many companies were formed. Much stock was sold. More wells were drilled. Just as Beaumont became the first oil boom town on the Gulf Coast, so did Red Fork become the first in the Mid-Continent region. This unwarranted boom, combined with the development of pools to the north at Alluwe and Chelsea, caused many men to look rapaciously towards the lands of the Five Civilized Tribes.

In 1902 the Department of the Interior, influenced by the Red Fork boom, approved the first lease of Indian lands in the Indian Territory. The boom effect was felt especially in a zone extending northward to the Kansas line. By 1904 the oil industry had become increasingly important in the Oklahoma and Indian territories. Most of the Indian allotments had been assigned, and the Department of the Interior removed some of the restrictions on leasing, an action which permitted increased exploratory drilling. Prospectors drilled wells near Guthrie, Oklahoma City, McCloud, Shawnee, Blackwell, Chandler, and Cushing. One startling well produced a large quantity of oil near the village of Cleveland, and many wells were drilled

---

[1] A common story, which seemingly cannot be substantiated by the records, is that this well was drilled by Dr. Fred S. Clinton, of Tulsa, and Dr. John C. W. Bland, of Red Fork, both of whom were practicing medicine. Both men knew of the well, and it is most likely that they were of considerable assistance. Bland's influence may be seen in the fact that the well was on his wife's homestead allotment.

24

on lots in the town; consequently all of Pawnee County was leased. At Newkirk the owner of a small well sold oil to his neighbors at twenty cents a gallon. The Prairie Oil and Gas Company was given a permit by the Department of the Interior to lay a pipe line across the Osage Reservation for the transportation of Indian Territory oil to Neodesha, Kansas. There were less than five hundred active wells in Oklahoma in 1904, but the year's production was more than one million barrels, a total that raised the territories from twelfth to ninth rank among the oil-producing states.

A year later, in 1905, the total yield of petroleum in the United States appeared to be in excess of the consuming capacity of the country, especially with the Indian and Oklahoma territories contributing more than eight million barrels. In consequence the price declined sharply.

It was in 1905 that the amazing Glenn Pool was discovered in the Creek Nation about twenty miles from the little town of Tulsa. The discovery well was drilled by Robert Galbreath and Frank Chesley, who were seeking to extend the production of the Red Fork Pool. The first three wells were progressively larger producers that attracted oil men from all parts of the United States. The Glenn Pool wells flowed by natural pressure, and hundreds of them were drilled with an average depth of 1,450 feet. The enormous flush production, combined with the limited transporting facilities, caused the oil to sell at a level of thirty-one cents a barrel. When steel or wooden storage was not available, the petroleum was permitted to fill earthen reservoirs. Thousands of barrels of crude oil filled low places in the ground or ran down the creeks to the Arkansas River.

Sapulpa, a village at some distance, prospered, and called itself "the gateway to the oil fields." Businessmen at Tulsa, who were farther removed from the Glenn Pool excitement, constructed a comfortable hotel, which became an important factor in making that city the center of the Mid-Continent oil industry. Kiefer, previously a mere flag station on the railway, quickly became a community of several thousand persons, a majority of whom were young and unmarried men. The men worked twelve hours and spent much of the remaining part of the day seeking entertainment, generally far from cultural, in "the Bowery." The nights were often lighted by the glare of burning oil, from which the clouds of jet smoke blotted out the stars. The Glenn Pool continued to be the center of attention and to increase in production until the summer of 1907.

Not far from Ardmore, south of the Arbuckle Mountains, a well drilled by the Santa Fé Railroad in 1905 proved to be the discovery hole of the Wheeler Gas Pool, which eventually led to the opening of another large oil pool.

Chiefly because of the plentiful amount of oil from the wells of the Glenn Pool, a pipe line was constructed in 1906 to the Standard Oil Company's refinery at Whiting, Indiana. This pipe line definitely marked the beginning of the competition of the Mid-Continent area in the national petroleum market. The Prairie Oil and Gas Company invested about thirty-five million dollars in pipe lines and storage tanks with which to handle the petroleum. Neodesha became a headquarters in transporting the output of Kansas and the Indian and Oklahoma territories. The focal point remained the Glenn Pool, where millions of barrels of oil were brought to the surface of the earth as the producing area was extended toward the towns of Mounds and Sapulpa. The Glenn Pool waste continued to be fabulous, as additional oil was discovered by exploratory wells. Several pools were found near Bartlesville, while other discoveries between 1904 and 1907 included Bald Hill, Chicken Farm, Lucky, Oologah, Dewey, and Morris. The Texas Company and the Gulf Oil Corporation began building pipe lines to carry Glenn Pool oil to the refineries and exporting terminals on the Gulf of Mexico.

Continued development of the oil industry on Indian land was presaged by an investigation by the Committee on Indian Affairs of the United States Senate, causing the Department of the Interior to remove more of the restrictions on the property of the tribesmen. Leases of Choctaw and Chickasaw land were permitted. The roll of the Osage tribe was closed January 1, 1906, and preliminary steps were taken to divide the royalty income of the reservation among the members. It was in 1906 that the original blanket lease of the Osage Reservation expired, but, after a hearing by the Department of the Interior, the contract was renewed with the Indian Territory Illuminating Oil Company. The new lease was reduced to include only the eastern side, approximately half, of the reservation, which already held 783 wells. It was arranged that the members of the Osage tribe should share equally in the receipts of the oil and gas, which were held in common, a fact that was to give them a reputation for being immensely wealthy. At one time this was true, but, by and large, it is no longer the case.

With the Indian Territory included, Oklahoma became a state in 1907, and that year it led the nation in the production of petroleum with 43,524,128 barrels. The value of the output, of which 19,926,995 barrels came from the Glenn Pool, was fixed at $17,513,000. The peak of the Glenn Pool flow came in 1907, when a total of 3,956 wells had been drilled in Oklahoma. Production from the Glenn Pool was so abundant and the marketing facilities so limited that the price of oil at Kiefer continued to drop. More

27

waste resulted, especially when many of the earthen tanks overflowed, and one lease became more valuable for the oil that it caught in a ravine than for the output of its wells.

Laws and regulations in 1908 caused increased activity among oil operators in the new state of Oklahoma. First the Department of the Interior required drilling within a year after the approval of a lease on Indian land. As most of the oil in Oklahoma was found on land owned by Indians, many of whom were wards of the United States, the regulation had the effect of producing a large amount of petroleum, regardless of supply, storage, or price. Next the legislature of Oklahoma enacted a law that had the effect of placing the estates of many Indians under the administration of the county courts. This law brought sad results for the Indians, hundreds of whom had no understanding of the laws and customs of the white men and little knowledge of the value of the petroleum that might be under their allotments. Some of the new county judges were unscrupulous, and the former Indian Territory was permeated with white attorneys who greedily disregarded the property rights of the allottees. Through corrupt connivance the law permitted a change in landownership, which in the course of time was to make the valuable lands of the Five Tribes, especially in the districts where oil was discovered, an area with a high ratio of absentee ownership and farm tenancy. Restricted members of the Five Tribes under the guardianship of the Union agent at Muskogee received a total of $1,692,627 in royalties in 1908.

A third law that interfered with the petroleum industry was one that prevented the piping of natural gas out of the state. It had been the belief of the lawmakers that the abundant gas of Oklahoma would attract manufacturers if it were kept within the state. Oklahoma had virtually no factories, and none of importance came, so the result was that most of the gas was wasted. In 1908 the gas field near Ada was discovered. Despite the retarding influence of the law, the Oklahoma gas brought its owners a revenue of $451,906 from domestic users. The total actual value of the year's gas production, however, was fixed at more than eight million dollars.

The more important liquid product of the Oklahoma oil pools was valued at more than sixteen million dollars. Petroleum from the Glenn Pool was being transported by three pipe lines in 1908. The Texas Company and the Gulf Oil Corporation were taking it south to the Gulf of Mexico, and the Prairie Oil and Gas Company was moving it north to Neodesha, Kansas, and to Whiting, Indiana. With the Glenn Pool producing 2,250,000 barrels daily, Oklahoma led the nation in quantity of oil produced, though it was third in the value of its output. Not only were several new pools opened in 1908, but two pipe lines in Washington County enabled that area to lead the state in production.

The year 1909 was exciting in Oklahoma, as a dozen new pools were discovered, making a total production of 47,859,218 barrels for the state, valued at $17,428,990. The yield was so great that the operators discussed plans that might be used to reduce drilling. They were irked by the fact that the Department of the Interior placed limitations on the laying of pipe lines across Indian land. The purchasers of oil were more seriously disturbed by the official suggestion that the pipe lines should be made common carriers and common purchasers. In 1909 there were 2,771 wells drilled, and only about two hundred of them failed to strike oil or gas.

The completion of the pipe line from the Glenn Pool to Baton Rouge in 1910 gave Oklahoma producers a larger market, with the result that the state rose to second place in the value of its petroleum. Oklahoma yielded virtually one-fourth of the nation's oil. Eleven new pools were discovered and 3,777 wells drilled. Tulsa gained additional significance in the industry in 1910 when Patrick J. Boyle established there *The Oil and Gas Journal,* a weekly trade magazine. While in 1912 the rapidly growing automotive industry worried about the fuel supply for its increasing products, nearly six thousand wells were completed in Oklahoma; production nevertheless declined.

The most copious pool for many years was discovered near the village of Cushing. Cushing was a rural trading center with two railroads where the farmers sold their produce and purchased manufactured goods. Eastward lay the low, stony hills that had been a poor part of the Creek Nation, some of which had been allotted arbitrarily to recalcitrant Indians and some sold to farmers. About a dozen miles from Cushing lived Frank Wheeler, a mason, with his family of many children, for whom he struggled to earn a living as a farmer. Among the elements of society that Wheeler disliked the most were those men who traveled about the country leasing land for exploratory oil wells. In the evening of a dour day late in 1911, a stranger stopped at the Wheeler farm and asked to spend the night.

The visitor was Thomas B. Slick, to whom the night's lodging might have been refused if Wheeler had known he was seeking leases. When Slick left the next day he had a lease, and began at once to search for finances with which to drill a well on Wheeler's farm. The storekeepers at Cushing refused to risk the few necessary thousands of dollars, but Slick acquired the money from a Chicagoan, Charles B. Shaffer, who was interested in several eastern oil pools. Quietly the well was drilled until the oil fraternity at Tulsa showed curiosity, especially when they learned that Slick would tell nothing. Slick's reticence promoted a burning anxiety for information, particularly when it became known that the Prairie Oil and Gas Company was planning a pipe line toward the Wheeler well.

The curiosity became insatiable when a lease on a small plot of Indian land near the well was sold for an enormous price. Tulsa oil men then attempted to visit the Wheeler well in person to gain information, but on arriving at Cushing they found that all the livery rigs had been hired by Slick and locked in the stables. Some of the eager men, however, did succeed in seeing the well, and assured themselves that it was a good one. They began to buy leases. They were not through with the difficulties arranged by Slick, however, for he had sent all the notaries away on a paid vacation trip. He leased land in every direction before the Wheeler well was finally completed and opened to production. The policy of secrecy had acted as a magnet; oil men of all types hastened to gain a foothold in the region east of Cushing.

Drilling was hurried with feverish intensity as additional machinery was placed on the locations. Machinery supply houses opened branches at Cushing, while carpenters nailed houses together and great teams pulverized the roads dragging heavy wagons loaded with iron pipe and rough oilfield equipment. As the pool was developed, it was not unusual for a well initially to produce fifteen thousand barrels of petroleum a day. As a source of gasoline the Cushing crude was nearly equal to that of Pennsylvania. Many of the Creek Indians who had refused to select their allotments now became rich from the very poor land that the government agents had assigned to them. One allotment produced millions of dollars worth of petroleum. And as if to reassure the automobile industry, Charles N. Gould, former director of the Oklahoma Geological Survey, announced that the state held enough oil to keep the drillers busy for half a century.

31

Flush Production

Geological departments were being established by the larger oil companies in 1913, a year in which Oklahoma produced more than one-fourth of the nation's oil. With the Cushing Pool growing in size and importance, Oklahoma wells yielded a total of 63,579,384 barrels, more than two-thirds of the output of the entire Mid-Continent region. The Cushing Pool, much the largest oil-producing area yet discovered, reached a length of more than seven miles and was three miles wide. A barrel of oil from it sold for $1.05 plus a bonus. When it reached the peak of production, the crude from the Cushing Pool provided more than one-half of the gasoline of the United States. It was in 1913 that the United States Navy, with 109 vessels operated by oil-burning engines, investigated the feasibility of laying a government pipe line from Oklahoma to the Gulf of Mexico, so that it would always be assured of an adequate fuel supply. At Cushing much of the petroleum was brought from the wells by an immense amount of gas under great reservoir pressure. As there was little market for the millions of cubic feet of gas, it was permitted to blow into the air as rapidly as possible. This was the accepted practice at all the oil pools, but the quantity wasted at Cushing was exceedingly great.

The desire to create a new Oklahoma county was a political child of the Cushing Pool, where it was believed at one time fifty thousand persons were living. Near the center of the field the town of Drumright sprang up, and in the course of a few months it contained stores and businesses of all varieties, excepting a bank, which was the last concern to be established. The difficult roads and the distances to the three nearest county seats, Chandler, Stillwater, and Sapulpa, caused dissatisfaction. The movement for a new county gained strength at Drumright and Cushing. A special census was taken of the counties which would be affected, to ascertain whether the legally required number of citizens would be left in the reduced units. A serious campaign was conducted by the proponents of the new political unit, which was to be called Shaffer County in honor of Charles B. Shaffer, who had financed the Wheeler well. It was declared that Shaffer County would be created free of debt yet containing millions of dollars worth of taxable property which would make it the richest in Oklahoma. Payne County, which would have lost territory through the creation of the new unit, confused the issue by conducting an election on a proposal to move its seat of government from Stillwater. The vote on the Shaffer proposal was held near the end of 1913, but the count was not conclusive enough to prevent a contest. The ballots were canvassed, and early in 1914 Governor Lee Cruce announced that the voters had failed to create Shaffer County.

The Cushing Pool continued, in 1914, to be the center of national interest. It contained more than seven hundred wells, and the daily production increased until an average of 225,000 barrels was reached. The pipe lines were unable to transport such a quantity of petroleum, so a large amount was stored at four large tank farms. During 1914 the Cushing Pool alone produced 17 per cent of the nation's oil, causing the price of crude petroleum to drop from $1.05 to seventy-five cents in a period of twenty-two days. Later the Cushing oil was sold for fifty-five cents a barrel. In order to raise the price, some of the Cushing producers proposed erecting a co-operative tank farm for withholding some of the petroleum from the market. As the output each day continued to increase, an effort was made to curtail production by a voluntary agreement among the operators. When this proposal proved ineffective, the Oklahoma Corporation Commission issued an order limiting the spacing and drilling of new wells.

In May, 1915, the Cushing Pool reached the height of its production with an output of more than three hundred thousand barrels of petroleum daily. Then it dropped abruptly. The decline of the Cushing output increased the demand for other crude oils, resulting in higher prices.

While the near-by pool was causing the town of Cushing to grow rapidly, to the north, in Kay County, Ponca City also was quickly becoming an oil town. East of Ponca City in the Osage country the Springer Pool was discovered. This pool was the direct result of geological study, and consequently the industry recognized the practical value of science in seeking petroleum. Searchers for petroleum were busy, especially in southwestern Oklahoma near the towns of Loveland, Lawton, Frederick, and Duncan. At Ardmore, in the southern part of the state, Roy Johnson, publisher of a little newspaper, and Wirt Franklin, a young attorney, with several others formed the stimulating nucleus of an oil company. They proposed to investigate the discovery made about two decades before by the earlier driller, Palmer. Thousands of acres surrounding the Palmer well were leased by the Johnson-Franklin organization. After a great deal of negotiating, a share in the acreage was assigned to the Red River Oil Company, the president of which, J. M. Critchlow, a former minister in Pennsylvania, owned a drilling rig. In return, Critchlow agreed to drill a well.

That well became the discovery hole of the mighty Healdton Pool, which reached its peak during the decline of the Cushing Pool. The oil from the first Healdton well was examined superficially by officials of the Magnolia Petroleum Company, who did not hesitate to say that they would buy all they could get. The wells were about one thousand feet deep, and the production cost of the oil consequently was only about twenty-five cents a barrel.

Demands Spur Production

The Mid-Continent oil was generally selling for about one dollar a barrel, which indicated that the Healdton oil would be particularly profitable. A pipe line from Texas was started by the Magnolia Company, and the many small lease holders of the Healdton Pool industriously drilled wells as rapidly as possible. By the summer of 1914, the 120 companies in the field claimed a daily potential production of several thousand barrels.

In the development of the Healdton Pool, John Ringling, the circus magnate, financed the beginning of a railroad called the Oklahoma, New Mexico, and Pacific, which was to run west from Ardmore. Jake L. Hamon, a promoter of remarkable ability, was Ringling's agent and president of the organization. While the railroad was under construction, the need for it became increasingly important as the Healdton Pool was developed. Finally it was built as far as the little village of Ringling. Half a day was consumed by the trip on a combination freight and passenger train operated from Ardmore.

The roads from Ardmore to the pool were deep in dust in dry weather and in almost impassable mud when there was rain. Several rough little towns sprang up in the oil field itself. The toughest one was called Ragtown until it gained the dignity of a post office; then its name was changed to Wirt, for Wirt Franklin, co-discoverer of the pool. Carter County, in which the pool was discovered, gained a reputation for the lawlessness of its oil-field workers and the bravery of its peace officers. On the leases of the Red River Oil Company, owned by the former minister Critchlow, all operations were suspended on Sunday in order that the employees might attend religious services, in devout contrast to the ordinary habits of some other citizens of the area.

The comparative inexpensiveness of the wells attracted

35

many men with limited finances. Healdton became known as the poor man's pool, because of the large number of independent operators. Wells could be drilled there for five thousand dollars, causing an involved and troublesome situation to develop when a large number of holes had been made. The operators had been stimulated in their drilling by the plan of the Magnolia Pipe Line Company to buy their oil. The statement of the company had been based on a superficial examination of the petroleum, but a laboratory analysis showed that it contained both asphalt and sulphur, which involved difficulties in refining. Consequently the Magnolia hesitated to purchase the output of the pool, and when the wells were yielding ten thousand barrels of oil daily the pipe line took only four thousand. The producers accused the purchasing company of unfair treatment and complained to the Oklahoma Corporation Commission. The state regulatory body investigated the situation, and Oklahoma Attorney General Charles West filed a suit against the Magnolia Company.

The company was charged with discriminating among the producers and with undue restraint of trade. Then, at the direction of a United States Senate resolution, the Federal Bureau of Corporations sent investigators to study the marketing conditions at the field. The affair became further involved when some of the producers met at Oklahoma City and planned a program which they believed would remedy the situation. The producers agreed that the Federal government should be urged to construct a pipe line to the Gulf of Mexico as an outlet for Healdton. In addition to Federal ownership of a transporting system, they proposed that all pipe lines be placed under the control of the Interstate Commerce Commission as common carriers. A third important proposal would have barred the pipe-line companies from entering the producing division of the industry.

The Cushing Pool after it crossed the Cimarron River

A portion of the Healdton Pool

Burkburnett wells sprang up in front yards and back yards . . .

. . . while in Oklahoma City they are neighbors to skyscrapers

Finally, the conference proposed that the Federal government should maintain a laboratory to analyze different oils and to disseminate information of value to the entire industry. But in May the Magnolia Pipe Line Company reached an understanding with the producers of the Healdton Pool whereby the firm agreed to take eight thousand barrels of oil daily and to increase its purchases gradually. The suit of Attorney General West became ineffective because the charge of discrimination was dropped when the compromise agreement was reached.

The Bureau of Corporations meanwhile found that because of the unreliability of the records and the unsettled question of what legally constituted discrimination a positive statement of a case was impossible. The investigation disclosed that the Healdton crude oil was of distinctly less value than several other oils that were available to the pipeline company. The gasoline and kerosene value of the Healdton oil was small, and the lubricating qualities added little to its value. The Oklahoma Corporation Commission used the compromise agreement of the Ardmore Producers Association and the Magnolia Pipe Line Company as the basis for an order that was intended to regulate the Healdton Pool. But despite the poor quality of the oil and the congestion already existing, the order permitted more drilling.

With the increase in the demand for gasoline, resulting partly from the World War in Europe, and the decline of the Cushing Pool, the Healdton Pool grew in importance. Many of the laborers and much of the equipment were moved from Creek to Carter County, where there were nearly five hundred wells and six hundred locations for more. The operators at Healdton, eager to dominate the Mid-Continent market, believed that a great increase in production there would prevent the development of another large pool. It was thought that the oil-producing horizon was in some cases three hundred feet thick. Already forty-two sections of land had been proved productive. Although Healdton production costs amounted to less than thirty cents a barrel, the producers were not willing to accept thirty cents for their petroleum. They raised funds and hired attorneys to go before the Oklahoma Corporation Commission to plead for an officially fixed minimum price of at least fifty cents. While these plans were being made the purchasers began to raise the prices, so in a short time the Healdton oil was selling for fifty-five cents a barrel. To give an additional outlet to the area, a refinery was planned at Gainesville, Texas, with a pipe line across the Red River to the Healdton Field. Only about one-half of the production of the Healdton wells, which yielded fifty thousand barrels of crude petroleum daily, was being sold.

One of the exploratory wells of 1914 was drilled near the village of Paden, nearly thirty miles from the huge Cushing Pool. It resulted in a thoroughly false excitement because of the mystery that surrounded it. The well was drilled by a local firm and the Prairie Oil and Gas Company, when suddenly the operations were stopped and the casing capped. The fact that oil had been encountered became known, and lease buyers paid the landowners of the vicinity more than two hundred thousand dollars for mineral contracts. After several months the well was opened to be completed, and, to the amazed disappointment of all, it was dry.

In 1914 Cato Sells, Commissioner of Indian Affairs, announced that he intended to be cautious in the negotiations surrounding the renewal of the lease of the Osage Reservation to the Indian Territory Illuminating Oil Company. The second ten-year lease would expire in 1916, and many members of the Osage tribe believed the Indians would receive more money if the contract were not renewed. The first lease covered the entire reservation, and despite the objections of some Osages it had been renewed, but only for about half the land of the tribe, or 680,000 acres. Hearings on the renewal of the lease were concluded in June, 1915, when the Department of the Interior agreed with the Osage Tribal Council that the Indian Territory Illuminating Oil Company was not needed as an intermediary. Rules for handling the Osage leases through the Indian Agency at Pawhuska were formulated. It was planned that the mineral rights would be sold at public auction to the highest bidders. Different leases would be arranged for oil and gas. The oil royalty to the Indians was increased from one-eighth to one-sixth and one-fifth of the production, depending on the size of the wells. By the new arrangement the Osages received a larger share of both the oil and gas revenues.

The oil industry of Oklahoma led the nation in 1915 in both the quantity and the value of its production. The 15 oil pools discovered that year brought the state's total to 136, and there were 30,500 active wells. Refiners anticipated an increasing demand for the petroleum and its manufactured products as a result of the war in Europe. Some of them predicted that the price would increase to $1.50 a barrel. Before the year closed the general price level had improved. Additional verity was given the predictions of the refiners by the fact that the United States Navy arranged for the privilege of purchasing the oil of Osage County in case it was needed. At Oklahoma City the Attorney General announced that the Secretary of State did not have authority to charter pipe-line companies that did not agree to act as common carriers. The Corporation Commission issued an order prohibiting the storage of petroleum in wooden or earthen tanks because of the great waste through evaporation.

Flush Production

Considerable discussion was aroused at this time by a well near Blackwell, Kay County, which was 3,367 feet deep. It had reached an oil-bearing horizon, later recognized as Ordovician, which was deeper and older than previously identified productive formations. A producing sand twenty-seven feet in thickness was found, which led to the conclusion that deeper drilling would continue to produce more oil. Previously Kay County had been considered about as far west as the search for petroleum could logically be carried. The depth of the well at Blackwell, however, prevented more holes from being drilled until improved machinery became available.

Although not as spectacular as in Oklahoma, the oil industry in the other southwestern states had been continuously active. The first fifteen years of the century were comparatively quiet ones for the industry in Kansas. That state, with a year's output of 77,714 barrels, was second to Texas in the production of petroleum in 1900. The refinery at Neodesha was operating at capacity, and formed the center of interest in the state. The problem of transportation was solved in Kansas with the organization in 1900 of the Prairie Oil and Gas Company, a Standard Oil subsidiary which constructed and operated pipe lines and entered the producing division of the industry. Exploratory activity led to the discovery in 1902 of oil and gas near Erie, where thirty-five wells were drilled. The Bolton Pool was found, causing the Prairie Company to start using its first pipe line for supplying the Standard Oil Company's refinery at Neodesha. The total Kansas production was more than three hundred thousand barrels of oil, and the gas that year was valued at $824,431. The pipe line was extended in 1903 from the Neodesha area to the new pools at Chanute and Humboldt. Fourteen hundred wells were drilled and the state's total production increased to 932,-

40

Demands Spur Production

214 barrels, three times that of the previous year. Kansas gas continued to be more valuable than the oil, however, and in 1903 it was sold for $1,123,849 while the petroleum brought only $988,220.

Nearly two thousand square miles of Kansas in eleven counties were covered by the oil industry in 1904. The refinery at Neodesha was taking its daily capacity of 2,500 barrels of crude oil, and a plant double that size was operating at Kansas City. The Kansas City refinery was supplied by a pipe line 116 miles long. Kansas produced more than four million barrels of petroleum, and a pipe line to transport the increased output was started from Kansas City to Whiting, Indiana. The consumption of gas in Kansas in 1904 displaced a quantity of coal with an estimated value of $2,275,875.

It was hoped that the congested storage facilities would be relieved in 1905 when the Prairie Oil and Gas Company completed its first pipe line to Whiting. The line, 544 miles long, would move thirteen thousand barrels of petroleum daily. Production in the state was increased in 1905 when two hundred wells were drilled in the new Bolton Pool. Two years later there was little drilling because the price of petroleum did not justify the risks; because of the price level, in fact, the Kansas output was reduced to little more than 1,500,000 barrels. More wells were abandoned than drilled in 1908, although at Iola a well believed to be the deepest west of the Mississippi was completed. It was 3,434 feet deep and went 2,400 feet below the well-known horizons.

Higher prices in 1911 stimulated drilling which resulted in new discoveries that served to check the decline in the production of petroleum in Kansas. Two years later there were twice as many wells drilled as had been completed in 1912. The pools at Eldorado and Augusta were

41

developed in 1914 and 1915. The output of Kansas was increased 30 per cent in 1914 when there were about 3,500 active wells. The development of the Eldorado Pool and the eight-thousand-barrel wells at Augusta were the center of attention.

CHRONOLOGICAL TABLE
OF TEXAS OIL POOLS, 1901–15

Pool	Year Discovered	County and Region
Spindletop	1901	Jefferson, Gulf Coast
Powell	1901–1917	Navarro, east
Sour Lake	1902	Hardin, Gulf Coast
Petrolia	1904	Clay, north
Beaver Switch (Electra)	1909–1911	Wichita, northwest
Burkburnett (Schmocker No. 1)	1912	Wichita, northwest

(There is uncertainty as to whether the discovery of Sour Lake was in 1901 or 1902; of Petrolia, in 1902 or 1904.)

Far more significant than Kansas, the Texas oil industry was second only to that of Oklahoma in importance between 1901 and 1915. The exploratory drilling near Corsicana in 1901 produced the Powell Pool, where the wells were about seven hundred feet deep. Most of the Corsicana-Powell oil was refined at Corsicana, but several marine shipments were made. Toward the west, oil ruined the water in several ranch wells of Wichita County, and one great landowner, W. T. Waggoner, later to become quite rich through petroleum, was furious when at hog-killing time a new well produced oil. In 1902 the cheapest oil in the United States was in Texas, where the supply appeared to be the most plentiful, for Spindletop alone reached a peak of 17,500,000 barrels that year. Petroleum was found in thirty-nine Texas counties in 1902, with the wells at Sour Lake reaching gusher proportions. A pipe line was laid to the Sour Lake

Pool. While Texas was leading the southwestern states in the production of petroleum, its gas was valued at only $14,953.

Sour Lake continued to hold attention in 1903 when a lease of 850 acres was sold for nine hundred thousand dollars. One hundred and fifty wells were drilled in the pool, and the resulting flood of petroleum caused one lot of a hundred thousand barrels to be sold for only one thousand dollars, a rate of one cent a barrel. Another coastal pool was discovered in Texas at Batson Prairie, and a pipe line was constructed to the near-by Saratoga Pool. Oil in the water wells of Wichita County, in northern Texas, was responsible for the organizing of the Wichita Oil Company, a firm that planned to drill eleven wells. Those wells were the basis for founding the town of Petrolia in 1904. Texas production nearly reached eighteen million barrels in 1903 and was valued at $7,517,479.

At Beaumont thirty-four million dollars had been invested in refineries, pipe lines, and loading docks by 1904. From Texas ports more than ten million barrels of crude oil were exported by tank ship. Most of the petroleum was brought to the docks by the five hundred miles of pipe lines that served the industry, and the hundreds of railway tank cars also in use. Eighty wells were drilled during the year at Petrolia, definitely opening a new region to oil production. The Petrolia wells produced only 65,455 barrels, but the total for all of Texas was 22,241,413 barrels of petroleum with a valuation of $8,156,220.

The Dayton and Humble pools were producing in 1905 on the Texas Coast, and the second of those areas yielded a total of more than 15,500,000 barrels of petroleum during the year. Twelve pipe lines assisted in moving 28,-136,189 barrels from the wells of Texas in 1905, when the state, producing one-fifth of the nation's oil, was exceeded only by California. The average price of the Texas oil was twenty-six cents a barrel, making the total value of the product more than $7,500,000.

The only Texas coastal pool that did not decline in production in 1906 was Saratoga, where the large leases tended to prevent pepperbox drilling. The fourth petroleum-producing area in Texas was initiated in 1907 when the Mission Pool was opened near San Antonio. The most significant event of 1908 in Texas was the discovery of gas by a rancher living near Laredo, a city that was soon supplied with gas for domestic fuel. The Goose Creek and Markham pools were discovered on the coast, causing Texas oil men to fear that overproduction would result. Most of the railroads in Texas were burning the state's crude oil in their locomotives by 1908, when the total output was 11,206,464 barrels. The next year W. T. Waggoner got one hundred thousand dollars from an oil company for a lease on his 250,000-acre ranch in five counties near Wichita Falls. The company then drilled five wells near Beaver Switch. This beginning definitely anticipated a series of oil fields that were to reach a climax with the Burkburnett-Ranger frenzy a decade later. Despite the Wichita County wells and the discovery in the southern part of the state of the Somerset Pool, the oil production of Texas declined. A notable invention was made in 1909 when H. R. Hughes devised the two-cone rotary bit to replace the often unsatisfactory fishtail. This technological achievement made the much deeper wells of later decades a possibility.

The general public was attracted to the Waggoner ranch area in 1911 when the Electra Pool, named for the cattleman's daughter, boomed. Dealers in leases rushed to the district where prices for the drilling privilege ranged from $150 to $500 an acre. Petroleum at Electra, formerly Beaver Switch, was found at four depths. So eager was the near-by city of Wichita Falls to become an oil town that the chamber of commerce offered a bonus of five thousand dollars for the first well within six miles. It was at this time that the first Burkburnett well was started, but it was not completed until 1912 and was not a sensation. Drillers were actively seeking oil in fifty-six counties in 1911, but Texas was ranked seventh among the petroleum states with the value of the year's output at $6,554,552.

A sensational boom was to develop later, as a result of the success in 1912 of the eleventh well drilled near Mexia, Texas. But at this time the center of interest in Texas was in Clay and Wichita counties, around the Electra Pool, where 101 wells were drilled. A slump in the price of oil caused the excitement to subside despite the fact that millions of dollars had been invested after the Schmocker No. 1 was completed as a producer. The Schmocker well really was the discovery hole of the Burkburnett Pool, although that boom also was to come later.

Three additional oil pools were discovered in Texas in 1913, at Toyah in the west, Moran in the north, and Cow Bayou on the Gulf Coast. Exciting activity occurred in Wichita County in 1914, when the Iowa Park Pool was opened and fifty wells were drilled. The wells were from 140 to 500 feet deep. They cost only a few hundred dollars to drill, and produced an average of sixteen barrels of oil daily. The high gasoline content of the Oklahoma petroleum, particularly that from the Cushing Field, caused much of the Texas Gulf petroleum to be used as fuel oil without refining. Prospecting and drilling were going on in forty-three Texas counties in 1915, and the state's total production amounted to more than twenty million barrels.

Equaling those of Texas in importance, the developments in Louisiana during this fifteen-year period were far-reaching. The loose sandy formation from which the Jennings oil and gas came was responsible for the development of a screen to prevent the wells from choking. In 1902 Louisiana produced a commercial quantity of petroleum for the first time when the Jennings Field was enlarged and the state's production exceeded five hundred thousand

CHRONOLOGICAL TABLE
OF LOUISIANA OIL POOLS, 1901–15

Pool	Year Discovered	Parish and Region
Jennings	1901	Acadia, south
Anse-la-Butte	1902	St. Martin, south
Caddo	1906	Caddo, northwest
Vinton	1910	Calcasieu, Gulf Coast
Pine Prairie	1912	Caddo, northwest
De Soto	1913	De Soto & Red River, north
Crichton	1914	Red River, north

barrels. Pipe-line transportation to the Gulf of Mexico was provided. Several sugar refineries adopted oil in place of coal as their fuel. The Jennings Pool continued in importance in 1903, and the state's total output of 917,771 barrels was valued at $416,228. Louisiana was the only oil-producing state of the Southwest where no natural gas was sold. Gas was found at Raceland in 1904, but it was not commercialized. The total production for Louisiana that year amounted to 2,958,958 barrels, and at the Jennings Field more than three million barrels were held in wasteful earthen storage. More new pools were discovered in Louisiana in 1905, and for the first time gas, in the amount of $1,500, was sold.

It was in 1906 that the first important northern Louisiana well was drilled in Caddo Parish. It had an immense initial gas pressure that blew out a crater so large that the derrick fell into the hole. The gas was ignited and the well burned for months before the owners gained control of it. A new coastal pool attracted attention in 1907 when a three-thousand-barrel well was drilled at Anse-la-Butte. The well proved to be the sensation of the year. Louisiana oil sold for eighty-one cents a barrel, which was three cents less than Texas petroleum brought but about double the price received for the Glenn Pool product. Near Moorings-port, Caddo Parish, there was a boom in land prices in 1908 as a result of the previous discovery of petroleum. Nearly six million barrels of petroleum were produced at the coastal fields of Jennings, Anse-la-Butte, and Welsh, but the production in Louisiana declined.

The completion at Vinton, in 1910, of a gusher that produced twelve thousand barrels of petroleum daily aroused unusual interest. The first three wells at the Vinton Pool produced more than three thousand barrels each at a depth of about 2,225 feet. Three pipe lines were transporting Louisiana petroleum in 1910. One stretched from Baton Rouge, a refining center, to the Glenn Pool in Oklahoma. A second took the output of the Jennings Pool and other coastal areas to Beaumont for processing and exporting. Another connected the Caddo Pool, near Shreveport, with the Gulf of Mexico.

The activity of the oil industry in 1912 was focused on the Caddo Pool, where many wells were drilled in the waters of a large shallow lake. The prolific wells of the Caddo Pool wrested the state leadership of the industry from the earlier discoveries in the coastal district. At Pine Prairie, oil was discovered by the eighth well that had been drilled in three years. The Pine Prairie Pool and the development of the Caddo Lake area did not prevent Louisiana from declining in total production, however, and in 1912 it ranked sixth in quantity. A gusher near Mansfield in 1913 opened the De Soto Pool in northern Louisiana. The next year oil was

47

discovered sensationally in Red River Parish, at Crichton. In the entire state 566 wells were drilled. Drillers completed 422 wells in twenty-three areas in 1915. The output of Louisiana, to which the recent Crichton Pool alone contributed six million barrels, increased a great deal in this year.

While the other four southwestern states became definitely important as producers of petroleum, the development of the oil industry in New Mexico and Arkansas remained negligible. The "oiliness" of the water from the artesian wells at Portales, Artesia, and Roswell, New Mexico, led settlers in the Pecos River Valley to look for petroleum in 1901. The New Mexicans were so taunted by surface indications that in 1902 efforts were made to drill wells in seven counties. Oil was found in 1911 near Dayton, Raton, and Seven Lakes, but only from the first of these was the product sold. The industry in this state continued to be experimental through 1914, when one well was drilled, one was abandoned, and one was dry. Near Mansfield, Sebastian County, Arkansas, four wells were drilled in 1902. Sixty thousand acres of four Arkansas counties were leased in 1913. Four dry wells were drilled.

The total yield of the Gulf-Southwest states approached 150,000,000 barrels of petroleum, valued at more than $80,000,000, in 1915. During that year, while the production of the great Cushing Pool dropped, the price of oil increased from 40c to $1.20 a barrel. The petroleum of the Gulf Coast was consumed principally in the manufacture of lubricants and fuel oil, while gasoline was made from the Mid-Continent crude. Much gasoline came from the Oklahoma gas, and at the Cushing Field alone there were sixty-three casinghead plants. The rise in price followed a demand that came chiefly from the First World War and the rapidly growing number of motor vehicles. The motor vehicles had increased in a decade and a half from 8,000 to 2,445,666, but the growing demand for fuel had been more than met by the oil from the southwestern states.

While the cars of the motor manufacturers were establishing a major industry on the shores of the Great Lakes, the petroleum deposits of the Southwest were gaining a secure hold on the nation as gas, gasoline, and lubricants became a vital necessity in the life of the people. These two great industries of the United States developed together, each depending on and largely responsible for the other. Neither the automobile nor the oil industry could have reached its later significance independently.

It was during the swashbuckling early years of the twentieth century that a few fortunate small oil firms became large companies with great holdings and laid the foundations for national influence. It was during that same time that thousands of small investors lost their savings through speculative and risky drilling schemes. Many landowners throughout the six states, of course, became wealthy when petroleum was found on their property. It was a period of great personal fortunes and untold recklessness. Paralleling the immense economic, physical, and moral waste was the tremendous development of new wealth and resources, which offered employment to thousands while millions were supplied with previously unknown comforts and conveniences.

Petroleum in Abundance

URING the second fifteen years of this century, the southwestern oil industry became definitely complicated, involved in technological and scientific problems and entangled in political, social, and economic troubles. Before and after the United States entered the First World War, the producers of petroleum struggled against odds to take as much oil from the ground as the demand required, at the same time maintaining a profitable price level. During the European conflict they feared that Federal agencies might gain permanent control of the industry; consequently they organized to prevent such a change. Since millions of automobiles, hundreds of locomotives, and thousands of ships consumed petroleum as lubricants and fuel, statistically bent scientists issued doleful predictions that the oil supply would be consumed in a few years. Such forecasts were delightfully pleasing to the coal industry, which was depressed by the bitter knowledge that factories and homes were constantly turning to petroleum for power and heat.

Despite the forecasts of exhausted resources, the national multiplication of consumers stimulated the search for oil in the Gulf-Southwest. Voicing the optimism of the region was Joe Cathriner, at Houston, who in 1916 began publishing *The Gulf Coast Oil News*, which later was to become *The Oil Weekly*, an internationally known trade journal.

Petroleum in Abundance

CHRONOLOGICAL TABLE
OF TEXAS OIL POOLS, 1915–30

Pool	Year Discovered	County and Region
Goose Creek	1908–1917	Harris, Gulf Coast
Ranger	1918	Eastland, north
Burkburnett (townsite)	1918	Wichita, north
Hull	1918	Liberty, Gulf Coast
K-M-A (shallow)	1913–1919	Wichita, north
Westbrook	1920	Mitchell, west
Mexia	1921	Limestone, east
Panhandle	1921	Carson, Gray, & Hutchinson, Panhandle
Orange	1913–1921	Orange, Gulf Coast
Pierce Junction	1921	Harris, Gulf Coast
Big Lake	1923	Reagan, west
Nash	1924–1926	Fort Bend, Gulf Coast
Orchard	1924–1926	Fort Bend, Gulf Coast
McCamey	1925	Upton, west
Yates	1926	Pecos, west
Van	1929	Van Zandt, east
East Texas	1930	Rusk, Gregg, Smith, Upshur, & Cherokee, east

In Texas the production of nearly twenty-six million dollars worth of petroleum in 1916 gave that state third rank in the United States. At Electra the yield of oil was increased through deeper drilling, and some holes reached two thousand feet. South of Wichita Falls the citizens of Ranger subscribed money with which to drill for oil, but they failed to find it. The Texas and Pacific Coal Company, seeking fuel for the Texas and Pacific locomotives, discovered petroleum in a prospecting shaft ten miles east of Ranger. These were the first steps in a search that was to

51

develop later into one of the most exciting tumults of speculation in the history of the southwestern oil booms.

So eager were the citizens of Ranger to determine
whether petroleum existed in that area that a group of
them called on W. K. Gordon, the mining engineer and
general manager of the Texas and Pacific Coal Company,
to drill a well near Ranger. He agreed to if the residents of
Ranger would give him leases on more than ten thousand
acres of land in the district. Farmers, bankers, ranchers,
and merchants attended a mass meeting at Ranger where
leases were arranged on twenty-five thousand acres of land
surrounding the town. Gordon planned to put down four
wells. In the spring of 1918, near the edge of the town,
Gordon drilled the first well on the Walker farm. At a
depth of 3,400 feet a strong gas pressure was encountered,
and a broken bit caused the hole to be abandoned. The gas
was left to blow itself out. The next well was drilled southeast of Ranger on the McClesky farm, while Gordon sent
nightly telegraphic reports of progress to New York City.
When the McClesky well was dry at 3,200 feet, a message
arrived from New York ordering the drilling to be stopped.
Gordon read the telegram, and then on his own responsibility told the crew to drill two hundred feet deeper. The
McClesky well became a gusher. At about the same time,
a rumbling awakened the residents of Ranger, who discovered that the Walker well was spouting oil instead of
wet gas. Gordon's first well had been abandoned as a thirty-
five-thousand-dollar loss, only to become profitable.

Gordon's discovery in 1918 coincided with a peculiar
national situation, the fear that there would be a shortage
of oil with which to pursue the war in Europe. Three an-
nouncements were publicized supporting the possibility of
an oil famine. In a New York newspaper an article dole-
fully avowed that the petroleum in storage had decreased

more than twenty-two million barrels. The Bureau of Mines of the United States Geological Survey asserted that the nation's underground reserves were nearly half exhausted. Statisticians of the Smithsonian Institution revealed figures indicating that there were only seventy barrels of petroleum available for each person in the United States. The price made the production of crude oil in 1918 immensely profitable, and the big wells that the Texas and Pacific Coal Company had drilled at Ranger created far more than a flurry of excitement.

Gordon's firm was reorganized and renamed the Texas and Pacific Coal and Oil Company. Capital stock amounting to six million dollars was issued, and a large amount was sold for nearly two thousand dollars a share. The holdings of the company were valued at $300,000,000, and a report became current that an offer of $120,000,000 for the properties had been refused. After the pioneer company in the pool sold leases to other companies, a strenuous competitive drilling campaign followed. At one time four hundred wells were being drilled at an estimated cost of five hundred thousand dollars a day. The Ranger district boom was at its height when hundreds of men demobilized from the American army hurried to the Texas town and entered the oil industry. Some of the leases in the productive area were sold for fabulous prices. It was reported that seven million dollars was refused for one lease of 160 acres. Men who were unable to pay the extraordinary prices for these leases drilled wells at a distance. By 1919 the oil-producing district about Ranger was eighty miles wide. During that year it produced several times as much wealth as California yielded in gold in 1849, or as the Klondike in its best year. By 1922 there were eight horizons yielding oil in the Ranger area; five were sandstone and three were limestone.

Flush Production

The widespread production of petroleum not only caused the village of Ranger to become a small city, but also affected the other towns of the district. Less than a dozen miles west of Ranger was Eastland, where building permits in one week amounted to almost five hundred thousand dollars. A few miles farther west was Cisco, which also became a busy little city. To the north and south as well the countryside was transformed. A farming community on Hog Creek, known as Hogtown, was overlooked by the large companies until several small operators had gained a foothold. The first effort to find oil there had been a community enterprise in 1914, when the Hog Creek Oil Company had been organized. Stock was sold, and the well drilled to about eighteen hundred feet. Had that well been on a different site it would have encountered oil. A second futile effort was made in the fall of 1917. When the discovery well itself reached a depth of more than 2,500 feet in September, 1918, the driller became disgusted at not finding oil. The bits were changed about midnight, and while the tool-dresser was busy at the forge sharpening the dull bit, the well blew in. First came a burst of gas, which was ignited by the flame of the forge. After about twenty minutes, oil followed the gas from the hole. The flames, which were some two hundred feet high, attracted the farmers, who came running clad only in shoes and breeches. A community ring on the telephone asked the wives to bring the children and their husbands' shirts and socks. A wagon made a circuit and picked them up. The next morning the pasture of Joe Duke's farm was filled with men, women, and children looking at the flaming oil well. Lease and royalty buyers hurried to Hogtown from Ranger.

Hogtown grew magically. Soon it outgrew its bucolic name and became Desdemona. The Desdemona Pool probably set a mark as a district for small operators. There

almost any sum was sufficient to finance a man's start in
the oil business, although his entry might coincide accurately with his exit. New oil companies came and went like
dew. Some were incorporated, some were not. The leases
were as varied in number, size, and importance as were the
companies that owned them. There were plots as small as
one one-hundredth part of an acre, while some covered
many acres. Royalty shares were sold in portions as tiny
as one eight-hundredth of an acre. The first oil was transported from the Desdemona Pool in large tanks mounted on
wagons. Later the Humble Oil and Refining Company and
the Magnolia Petroleum Company laid pipe lines to the
wells. Promoters organized a refining company and a pipe-
line firm, and under the cloak of a local man's honest reputation, sold stock. Both enterprises were boom bubbles that
burst when the stock was sold.

While at the Desdemona Field hundreds of wells were
being drilled and a stream of oil three feet deep was block-
ing a highway, at the nearby town of Dublin schemers were
selling stock in five refineries and a pipe-line company.
Since the pipe-line company proposed to bring natural gas
to the town for fuel, it became known as the "hot air" plan.
Promoters collected thousands of dollars for worthless
stock in companies that never entered business.

Lagging only a short time behind the stirring events in
the Ranger area was a parallel boom to the north about the
town of Wichita Falls. Petroleum had been previously discovered in Wichita County at Beaver Switch, or Electra.
Flurries of excitement had come and gone with the different
discoveries. It was in the spring of 1918, however, that the
mad rush to Burkburnett was started. At least four attempts to find oil near the townsite of Burkburnett had
been made before S. L. Fowler, a farmer, succeeded in
financing a well on his land. Dry weather and poor crops

had convinced Fowler that he should sell his land and move
to another climate, but his wife hoped there might be petroleum under the cotton patch. The Fowler Farm Oil Company was organized in May, 1918. Fowler gave the company a lease on 185 of his 1,200 acres, and two neighbors
added an additional 300 acres. Stock of the company,
capitalized at twelve thousand dollars, was sold to other
farmers.

As the drill went deeper and deeper into the earth, many
persons smiled at "Fowler's Folly." By July the well was
more than seventeen hundred feet deep, and the local residents were thoroughly skeptical. They had reason to be,
for at only five hundred feet the wells on the not far distant Sunshine Hill were good producers. Shallow holes to
the contrary, mockery of Fowler's well soon ended.

"Oil's flowing down the cotton rows," announced the
driller when he aroused Fowler from his bed on the night
of July 24, 1918.

So unexpected was this situation that adequate arrangements had not been made to take care of the gusher. Seven
two-inch pipes were connected with the well, and six of
them turned oil into storage while the seventh was permitted to run on the ground. The well was declared to be the
largest in the state north of the Texas and Pacific Railroad.
Near-by farms were leased for one thousand dollars an
acre, while town lots also were taken. Citizens of Burkburnett met with the city council and arranged to limit
the drilling of wells to one on each municipal block, the
profits to be shared proportionately by the landowners.
Bonuses as large as four thousand dollars were paid for
single lots, and drilling was started before ordinances
could interfere. The first three wells to be completed
were gushers. Drilling on large and small leases became
rapid. Lease prices jumped upward, as many more oil

companies were organized. Doctors, lawyers, preachers, bankers, salesmen, and merchants rushed to the village, which soon became a congested mushroom city of thirty thousand persons. Pipe lines were laid. Storage tanks were constructed. New wells were completed every day. All the townsite wells produced oil, so that by January, 1919, the pool was yielding more than forty-five thousand barrels daily.

In the spring of 1919 the Burk-Waggoner Company drilled a well more than three miles north of Burkburnett. On Easter morning, when it blew in at a rate of five thousand barrels daily, the company signed a contract for sixteen more wells. The firm then sold its holdings for two million dollars, which amounted to a profit of $3,333.33 for each one hundred dollars originally invested. In closing that sale a seven-thousand-dollar telephone toll was paid for keeping a line open to New York for two hours. This well was only one of the extensions which radiated from the Burkburnett Pool.

Another oil boom occurred in Wichita County in 1919, when the Kemp-Munger-Allen Company struck oil on the Munger ranch near Iowa Park. At Wichita Falls a stock exchange had been organized. Before the discovery, the shares of the K-M-A, as the company was known, had been selling below the par figure of one hundred dollars. With the announcement of the strike the price of K-M-A catapulted to $2,500 and more per share. The stock exchange was wild. Lease prices went to ten thousand dollars an acre, for oil was selling at three dollars a barrel.

With the intention of keeping the price of oil at that highly profitable figure, the Wichita County Oil Producers and Refiners Association was formed by a majority of the men in the industry. They signed an agreement not to sell their product below the posted price, a plan to prevent price-cutting as a result of the great flush production. Twenty-five refineries were erected and put into operation in the county. In April, 1919, dividends of more than $3,500,000 were paid by fifty-eight oil companies operating at Burkburnett. Nearly a thousand wells were drilled in that pool, causing a decline in production at the end of two years to about two barrels each a day. Those producers and refiners who did not make great dividends in the beginning were to find meager profits later.

While the attention of most of the industry was on the Ranger and Wichita Falls districts from 1917 to 1919, oil men were also busy in other parts of Texas. At Goose Creek, on the Gulf Coast, a well producing thirty-five thousand barrels opened a new pool in 1917. When that well showered the town with mud and crude oil, the thousand villagers of Goose Creek simply moved their homes to a more comfortable location. The discovery of the pool caused the population of the town to grow to fifteen thousand. In the Texas Panhandle young geologists studied Hutchinson County, where Charles N. Gould, Oklahoma geologist, urged drilling. A location selected by the Amarillo Oil Company near Amarillo produced ten million cubic feet of natural gas in 1918. On the Gulf Coast the Hull Pool, a salt dome, was discovered, and became one of the important events of the year.

Despite the increase in the price of crude petroleum in 1918, resulting chiefly from World War demands, drilling activity was hampered in Texas by increased costs of equipment and delay in delivery, higher wages and scarcity of labor, the influenza epidemic, and a paucity of water in several oil-producing regions. The demand continued in 1919, despite the end of the war, and that year the first suggestion was made to prorate production in Texas. The suggestion resulted from the congested situation when the

pipe lines were unable to transport all the oil at Burkburnett. There the producers objected to closing or choking
their wells for fear that residue would choke the pores of
the producing formation.[1] The largest casinghead gasoline
plant in the world was in operation treating gas from the
Burkburnett Pool, while five thousand miles of pipe lines
in Texas were moving a million barrels of oil daily toward
refineries. At Beaumont, three of the largest refineries of
the world were in operation in 1919. At the port of Galveston, storage tanks for one million barrels of oil were
erected for use in marine exportation.

In the western part of the state, the Westbrook Pool was
discovered in Mitchell County, a small area that in sixteen
years produced more than 7,800,000 barrels of oil. Pipe
lines were opened to the Ranger district by 1920, but at
Desdemona earthen storage still held three hundred thousand barrels. Some conception of the magnitude of the
search for petroleum in Texas is possible from the fact
that in ten counties it was estimated that more than
$1,040,000,000 was paid for leases on fifty-two million
acres. North of Burkburnett wells were drilled in the bed
of the Red River, resulting in a legal battle between Oklahoma and Texas to settle a definite boundary.

On land that rented for twenty-five cents an acre as a
cattle range, O. W. Killam drilled a well that struck oil
near Laredo in 1921. That was the first oil well in Zapata
County, where sixty thousand head of cattle roamed. Far
to the north of the Rio Grande, in the Panhandle, petroleum
was found in Carson County, to be followed by discoveries

[1] At the regular session of the Texas Legislature in 1917, authority to
regulate the pipe lines was conferred on the Texas Railroad Commission.—
Acts, 35th Legislature, Regular Session, 1917, Chap. XXX, 48. The statute
that first gave the Railroad Commission power to make and enforce rules
for the conservation of oil and gas became a law in 1919—see *Acts,* 36th
Legislature, Regular Session, 1919, Chap. CLV, 285.

in the neighboring counties of Hutchinson and Potter. Many previous efforts had been made to discover oil in West Texas, from Amarillo to the Rio Grande, but the region had gained the sobriquet of "Petroleum Graveyard of Texas." Now the established towns, such as Amarillo, grew rapidly, while a few new ones sprang into being. The most boisterous of the young municipalities, which became tough adults almost overnight, was Borger, which bore the name of its principal promoter, A. P. Borger. Not only did the developments near Amarillo attract great interest, but they stimulated the exploratory drilling and searching in other parts of West Texas with renewed vigor. Oil was discovered near Luling and Mirando City. On the Gulf Coast two new pools were opened at Orange and Pierce Junction in 1921; by that time there were forty-four known salt domes, of which seventeen were producing petroleum.

Drilling to three thousand feet brought a spectacular pool and boom rush to Mexia, not far south of Corsicana, in 1920. This area, the first of the great Balcones Fault pools, previously was a gas-producing one. The first oil well was only a small pumper, but the second, drilled by Colonel A. E. Humphreys, flowed at a rate of four thousand barrels daily. By 1921, when one well was yielding ten thousand barrels, the pool was six miles long and three miles wide. Congestion was rife. The town of Mexia now contained several oil-field supply houses and boasted one two-story building. Times were turbulent, and civil disorders caused Governor Pat M. Neff to declare martial law in two justice precincts of the booming flush field. Forty huge fifty-five-thousand-barrel tanks proved insufficient storage, despite efforts of the operators to pinch their wells and keep much of the oil underground. By the next year the Mexia output had declined nearly one-third, although the pool continued to produce for more than fifteen years. The Mexia Pool stimulated a search that resulted in delineating the Balcones Fault to Corsicana. A new field in the district was Wortham.

On a great stretch of dry Reagan County grazing land in the western part of the state, a small company started a well in September, 1921. It was hurriedly begun in order to validate a lease on more than four hundred thousand acres belonging to the University of Texas. The owners of the lease, Frank T. Pickrell and Haymon Krupp, christened their first well the Santa Rita, Saint of the Impossible, because the task before them was most difficult. They were able to drill only after selling several large blocks of the lease. About daylight, May 28, 1923, the well blew in from a depth of more than three thousand feet. The Big Lake Oil Company was organized and more wells were drilled; and in 1925 a pipe line was laid to the prolific field. Wells of the Big Lake Pool were nearly nine thousand feet deep in 1928, among the deepest in the country. From them the University of Texas derived a great fund and became one of the richest universities in the United States. Here again the industry followed the pattern of searching for more pools in the district of a great discovery. From Big Lake prospecting spread into Winkler and Pecos counties, which later were also to attract the attention of the industry. Several hundreds of miles to the north, the first flowing well was drilled in 1923 in Hutchinson County. A contract had already been signed in 1922 to pipe gas from the Panhandle to domestic and industrial consumers in the metropolitan district of the Middle West.

Two years of experimentation had proved, by 1924, that geophysical instruments were practical in finding the salt domes of the Gulf Coast. In that year many wells found oil as a result of geophysical exploration. The Nash, Orchard, and Long Point domes were discovered, the most popular instruments being the seismograph and the torsion balance.

In 1925 the production of petroleum in Texas showed an increase for the fifteenth successive year. Two important West Texas pools were discovered. George B. McCamey and L. P. Johnson found the McCamey Pool in Upton County and sold a 320-acre lease for five hundred thousand dollars. Fred Hyer was the chief of a group of oil men who drilled a shallow pumper on a lease of twelve hundred acres in Howard County. They sold their holdings for $250,000. The new fields in West Texas were important forerunners of later developments.

In the dry and lonely hills of Pecos County in southwestern Texas, Ira Yates and his wife, Ann, subsisted with their children on a debt-laden ranch in 1926. The land had been described as unfit for man or beast. In the interior of the ranch an exploratory oil well was drilled after much insistence by Yates. It was a great producer, and in a few days Yates sold leases for a fortune. His debts were reported to have been so numerous that he paid every claim that was presented even without proof of its validity. Additional wells, all with high productive capacity, outlined the oil pool. There was no near-by pipe line to transport the oil, and no law prevented its rapid production. Since the great Yates Pool threatened to cause a reduction in the price of petroleum, the Texas Railroad Commission was asked to restrict the output. That regulatory body issued orders limiting the production of the Yates Pool—the beginning of proration in the Texas oil industry. In addition to the Yates Pool, oil was found in 1926 on the Hendrick ranch in Winkler County, also in West Texas.

At Spindletop another boom in activities took place in 1925. Frank Yount and Marrs McLean drilled at an angle into the salt dome and had a good well at about three thousand feet. They drilled more wells and discovered oil at five levels. The price of Spindletop leases at once became speculative. One tract of seven acres sold for sixty thousand dollars. Some of the new wells had eight thousand barrels capacity, so that the yield of the field increased in June and July from twenty thousand to seventy thousand barrels. While Texas set a production record of more than 160,000,000 barrels in 1926, the attention of the industry continued to be held by Spindletop. That pool was producing one hundred thousand barrels of oil daily in September, with one well alone making twenty thousand. Oil men were prevented from leasing the highway at Spindletop only by Attorney General Dan Moody. One firm took two million barrels of oil from a lease of two acres. The wells at Spindletop declined gradually; the recession of the field was not as precipitous as it had been in 1901, because the gas had been held in the ground. By 1927 Spindletop had produced a cumulative total of more than twenty million barrels of oil.

Texans were startled in 1926 when it was announced that Edgar B. Davis had sold his oil-producing properties in the Luling district for twelve million dollars. Most of the bustling flush pools of that year were found in the Panhandle, where the excitement centered at Borger, now a town of thirty-five thousand persons.

The oil production of Texas exceeded two hundred million barrels in 1927, when men connected with the industry were active in all parts of the state. On the Gulf Coast the geophysical crews were busy seeking more salt domes, while in Zapata County the wells were yielding more than fifteen thousand barrels of oil and a billion cubic feet of gas each day. In that district land values had increased from the old ranching price of one dollar an acre to more than one thousand dollars in some cases. Transporting facilities had been improved farther west, and the pools of Crane, Upton, Crocket, Pecos, and Winkler counties were increasing in importance.

When the Texas industry led the nation in the production of oil for the first time in 1928, the West Texas wells yielded one-half of the state's total. The Hendrick Pool in Winkler County set a record by producing more than 6,500,000 barrels from 153 wells. Preposterous potential production was recorded at the Yates Pool when one well was deepened to more than eleven hundred feet and flowed seventy thousand barrels in a day. Another Yates well had a potential daily capacity of 169,374 barrels. The Yates leases were controlled by large companies, however; hence the development was orderly. The Big Lake Pool became the deepest in the world, with its high-quality petroleum coming from a horizon at more than eight thousand feet. As the production of the West Texas pools increased and continued to tax the marketing facilities, a widespread program of tank-building developed. In the Panhandle the gas became more valuable than the petroleum—large amounts were piped to distant cities for fuel, and natural gasoline extraction plants were erected to treat other great quantities. About one gallon of gasoline could be taken from the average thousand cubic feet of natural gas. Some of the Panhandle gas contained sulphur, which made it objectionable as domestic fuel, but from it carbon black could be made. By 1928 the manufacture of carbon black had become an important industry in this region.

Texas produced almost 300,000,000 barrels of petroleum in 1929, with more than 250,000,000 barrels coming from West Texas. The first wells were drilled in the Van Pool in 1929, and before the year closed there were 180. On the advice of scientists, five large companies had quietly leased the small farms of East Texas around the tiny village of Van in 1927. When the leasing had been completed the companies agreed that one firm, the Pure Oil Company, should handle the operation of the expected pool. The Van Pool was later to become outstanding as one of the earliest unit operations in the Southwest. Competitive drilling was eliminated, as were most of the characteristics of a new oil field, by the orderly and controlled development.

The operation of the Van Pool, where geese had previously kept the weeds out of the small fields, was hailed as scientific. The little village of Van, ten miles from the nearest railroad and sixty miles from Dallas, failed entirely to have a boom. In startling contrast to the situation here was the condition that had developed at Borger, several hundred miles to the northwest. An indication of the activity at Borger lies in the fact that during 1929 the railroad brought nearly four thousand cars of freight and took almost seventeen thousand carloads away from the town. The moving of petroleum was a big business in Texas in 1929, when the ports of that state saw 5,393,634 tons of oil exported. Oil and its products formed 56 per cent of the tonnage handled by Texas ports.

By 1930 there were 23,369 men operating oil and gas wells and 5,832 working at refineries in Texas. In the Panhandle ten carbon black plants were producing 60 per cent of the national output. The plants, most of which were in Hutchinson County, employed seventeen hundred men with a combined monthly pay roll of one hundred thousand dollars. Each day the plants produced five hundred thousand pounds of carbon black. Oil production records were being broken, and producers were frowning at the declining prices and the forbidding national economic outlook when a thoroughly upsetting well was drilled in East Texas.

On the little sandy farm of Daisy Bradford, in Rusk County, forty miles southeast of the Van Pool, C. M. ("Dad") Joiner drilled an oil well. Joiner had been one

65

of the numerous small producers in the Healdton Field in Oklahoma fifteen years earlier. Not only had geologists studied and condemned the new district, but many dry wildcat wells in the past had supported the decision of the scientists. Joiner had drilled two dry holes on the Bradford farm, so his financing capacity was limited as he stubbornly worked on the third. He traded shares in his lease for used casing. A banker from the small town of Overton worked as a laborer and his wife prepared the meals for Joiner's crew. The hole was more than 3,400 feet deep when petroleum flowed over the derrick on October 3, 1930. This was the first well in the mighty East Texas Pool, an oil-producing area that was to become the greatest in the history of the industry. Unlike many previous discoveries, this pool was not far from the great refineries of the Gulf Coast, and the discovery well was conveniently less than three miles from a railroad. An added attraction was the high quality of the oil. It was predicted that at least six exploratory wells would be drilled near-by within sixty days.

The second producing well of the district was drilled near the town of Kilgore, several miles from the Daisy Bradford No. 3. It had a capacity of fifteen thousand barrels a day. The third, with a potential capacity of ten thousand barrels, was near Henderson, several miles in another direction. Then came the lease buyers of large and small companies. The three wells were far enough apart to be discoveries of as many small pools, but they were good wells and there might be others. Near the end of December a fourth important well was completed ten miles from the Joiner discovery. This one flowed at a rate of twenty-two thousand barrels a day. Then, as all the wells produced from the same Woodbine formation, it was suggested that one immense pool was being tapped. The scramble for leases became intense. The area was one of small farms, hundreds of which were leased by little independent producers. These elements conspired to bring about intense competitive drilling, which in time was to release an upsetting quantity of petroleum on the national market.

Just thirty-seven days after the completion of Joiner's Daisy Bradford No. 3, the Texas Railroad Commission issued a state-wide order to the oil industry to reduce the amount of petroleum being produced. The order had little effect on East Texas operators, however, for so many exceptions were permitted that drilling and production were not checked.

CHRONOLOGICAL TABLE
OF OKLAHOMA OIL POOLS, 1915–30

Pool	Year Discovered	County and Region
Garber	1916	Garfield, north central
Burbank	1920	Osage, north central
Tonkawa	1921	Kay, north central
Wewoka	1923	Seminole, central
Cromwell	1923	Seminole, central
Seminole	1926	Seminole, central
Oklahoma City	1928	Oklahoma, central

While the Texas oil industry developed with magical rapidity during the second fifteen years of the century, similar events took place to the north in Oklahoma. With a total value of $128,463,805, the production of petroleum in Oklahoma in 1916 kept the state first among the oil producers. The Cushing Field grew with the development of the Shamrock extension, while in southern Oklahoma the yield at Healdton was increased. Oil was found at Garber, near Enid, a fact which proved that the Blackwell Pool did not mark the western extremity of petroleum production. The Garber Pool was a definite stimulus to deeper drilling. It had been thought that the three-thousand-foot wells of the Blackwell area defined the western edge of the Mid-

67

Continent oil-producing zone, but the Garber Pool was conclusive proof that the formations contained petroleum farther west and at greater depths. One of the Garber wells became the largest in the state, producing twenty-seven thousand barrels a day at more than four thousand feet. That led to deeper drilling throughout the Southwest, an era that opened as soon as the equipment manufacturers had devised heavier machinery. By 1918 seven oil-bearing horizons had been found in the Garber Pool, and multiple drilling was practiced.[2] In 1927 the operators at the Garber Pool claimed a record in the fact that they had discovered sixteen oil-producing horizons.

The second blanket lease of the Osage land expired in 1916, to be followed by a period of lease sales at public auction. A startling example of the profit which the new system was to bring the Indians was the case of one lease that sold in 1904 for twenty-five hundred dollars. In 1916 that lease was sold at auction for more than one million dollars. The Osage National Council offered eight sections of the tribal lands to the United States Secretary of the Navy in 1917. The intention of the Indians was to give the Federal government a reserve from which to take war supplies, but the officials did not accept the offer.

The Osage land was mapped by the United States Geological Survey in 1918, when the wells on the tribal holdings produced more than ten million barrels of oil. The treating plants in Osage County took nearly three million gallons of natural gasoline from twenty-four billion cubic feet of gas. The payments to the Osages reached the peak of $13,400 for each of the 2,229 headrights in 1926. A great deal of attention was attracted to Okmulgee County by the discovery of many small but highly productive pools. The

[2] Multiple drilling is the practice of making several wells, with different depths, at one location, so that oil may be taken from different horizons.

total output of Oklahoma in 1918 receded from the point reached the previous year, but for the fourth consecutive time it maintained the leading position among the states.

As the second decade closed, a field was opened in the western part of the state near Cement, and farther south, oil had been found near Duncan. There were more than twenty distinct pools in Osage County, where each big lessee was required to spend about one hundred thousand dollars annually on development. Another factor that contributed to the steady growth of the industry in this county was the insistence of the Secretary of the Interior on the leasing of one hundred thousand acres of the Indian land annually. One of the major Osage pools was the Burbank, discovered in 1920. In the six years after the discovery, thirteen auctions were held at Pawhuska to sell leases on the field. The highest price paid for one of the leases was $1,990,000 for 160 acres. During these six years, two thousand wells were drilled and more than 130,000,000 barrels of petroleum were taken from the area. The average spacing of the wells was one to each ten acres. With each Osage headright bringing an annual income of a few thousand dollars, the members of that tribe became known as "petrolecrats," while newspapers and magazines printed articles about their wealth. In 1925 the Osage lease form first mentioned casinghead gasoline, and the royalty on gas was fixed at one-eighth when commercialized.

Near the farming village of Tonkawa, with its population of about fifteen hundred, a well was drilled in 1921 that opened one of the important pools of the Southwest. The big development of the Tonkawa Pool, however, came after 1922. By 1924 the field, which covered more than five thousand acres, had yielded a total of more than thirty-four million barrels of oil from 663 wells. In 1923 the Tonkawa Pool was one of the eight highly productive ones that brought about a condition of overproduction. Nevertheless it was one of those that were highly profitable, for the oil was sold for more than two dollars a barrel. Tonkawa itself became a city.

It was in 1922 that Earl Sneed first conceived of an exposition for the oil industry at Tulsa, a city that had become the center of the Mid-Continent division of the industry. The first International Petroleum Exposition was held at Tulsa the next year. Tulsa had become a city of one hundred thousand since the discovery of oil at Red Fork.

Ten producing horizons were found in the Cromwell Pool, discovered in Seminole County in December, 1923. The first big well, yielding 4,600 barrels of high-gravity oil, was completed in March, 1924, about four months before the area reached its peak of 64,000 barrels. Several small wells attracted oil men to other parts of Seminole County. The first one of gusher proportions was drilled in 1926, and within a month the Seminole City Pool was yielding 218,000 barrels of petroleum. Soon there were nine distinct pools that became known as the Greater Seminole District, covering a producing area of more than twenty thousand acres. Before the end of 1926 there were eleven producing areas, of which seven were major pools. Since the price of oil had gone to more than $2.50 a barrel, the prolific Seminole wells became most attractive to speculators. But the flood of oil from Seminole caused a sharp price reduction in May. Royalty interest at the field sold for as high as eleven thousand dollars an acre, and some leases changed owners at a rate of sixteen thousand dollars an acre. The average lease at Seminole was eighty acres, but the largest contained 120 acres. At least two boom towns became important in the district: Bowlegs and Earlsboro.

In the scouting division of the industry a great change

occurred during the Seminole boom days. Previously the
large oil companies had kept scouts in various districts for
the purpose of maintaining intimate contact with the different developments. The scout's business was to be detective, spy, liar, or anything else necessary to keep his own
company informed regarding the activities or discoveries
of its competitors. The early scouts did strange things to
gain information. The large companies maintained private
telephone and telegraph lines to all the significant pools.
At the home office the scout was cursed for failing to send
a report, for the misplacing of a report, for an incorrect
report, for a late report. At times it appeared that he should
know everything. Some of the scouts sent daily reports and
others weekly messages. Some of the companies kept card
records of all the wells and were in a position to swap information. When the drilling at the Seminole Pool was active, it
became impossible for single scouts to gather information on
the hundreds of operations in progress at one time. From
necessity they organized themselves into a co-operative
body holding daily check meetings at which each scout
reported to the others on the activities of a division of the
pool. After the meetings each scout telephoned his information to his home office. Another change that gradually
affected the work of the scouts was the increasing importance of geological and other scientific knowledge, including the microscopic study of cuttings of formations brought
to the surface by drilling operations.

As the production of the Seminole Field continued to
increase with more drilling, chiefs of several major oil
companies conferred at New York in May, 1927. They
planned a program of restriction which they believed would
reduce the yield of the Greater Seminole District. They
selected Ray Collins, of Tulsa, and requested the Oklahoma
Corporation Commission to give him official authority as

71

umpire of the pool. Collins thus became a privately paid official of the state. Before he took charge, production at the field had risen to a maximum of more than half a million barrels a day. This was the first occasion of active proration in Oklahoma, being a voluntary move on the part of the major companies to reduce production.[3] From that time forward proration became a definite part of the oil industry in the state. The year's total Seminole yield was 10 per cent of the national production. It was the overshadowing figure of 136,000,000 barrels.

Oklahoma led the nation in the manufacture of natural gasoline in 1927, when plants were in operation in Creek, Seminole, and Osage counties. The natural gas of the Oklahoma oil fields contained an average of two gallons of gasoline for each thousand cubic feet.

Many men in the industry were already disturbed by the colossal and growing output of the Seminole Pool; soon a well was drilled near Oklahoma City that was destined to increase their worries. The first effort to discover petroleum near Oklahoma City had been a well drilled in 1903. It was followed by six other futile wells as the years passed. But in 1928 the Oklahoma City Pool was at last found when, at 6,400 feet, the Indian Territory Illuminating Oil Company's No. 1 Oklahoma City produced at the rate of five thousand barrels a day. The petroleum was of high quality and accompanied by a large volume of natural gas. Such a discovery, despite the expense of drilling more than six thousand feet, indicated that a major pool existed and that a large number of wells would be drilled. Men who were interested in limiting production for the purpose of preserv-

[3] Unsuccessful attempts by Oklahoma officials to control production had been made during the flush periods of the Cushing and Healdton pools. The control of the Seminole District differed fundamentally in the fact that the leaders of the industry actively supported a limitation of production.

ing the existing price structure arranged for rigid proration of the Oklahoma City Pool.

The first Oklahoma City well had cost more than $150,-000, but as more holes were drilled the expense declined. By 1930 more than six hundred wells had been drilled, and the potential capacity of the pool was estimated to exceed 1,500,000 barrels daily. Drilling continued rapidly, and the purchasers of petroleum reduced both their prices and the amounts they would buy. The field was not without sensations, though, for the immense pressure of the gas caused several of the wells to blow out of control. The most spectacular of these wells was the Mary Sudik. The "Wild Mary Sudik" was out of control for eleven days in March, 1930, during which time it produced more than two thousand barrels of oil an hour and more than two hundred million cubic feet of gas a day. The oil and gas sprayed the countryside, and with a wind it was carried for miles. Houses in neighboring towns were sprinkled by the crude oil. Earthen reservoirs were built and homes in the vicinity were abandoned, while the fire hazard caused all near-by drilling operations to be halted. The well was opened for the first time in September, producing more than a thousand barrels of oil an hour.

In Oklahoma 26,628 men were employed in the operation of oil and gas wells in 1930, and the refineries of the state required 2,048 workers. The oil industry supplied 65 per cent of the state's revenue in two taxes alone. The gross production tax yielded a total of ten million dollars, while the gasoline tax yielded twelve million. Oklahoma produced more petroleum than any other state from 1916 to 1922 (inclusive), chiefly because of hundreds of small pools. During the first three decades of the century the oil industry had spread from the shallow producing areas of the northeastern part of Oklahoma toward the west. For years the Blackwell Pool had been regarded as marking the western extremity of oil production, but by 1917 it was considered probable that petroleum-bearing formations would be found at greater depths in the western part of the state. After 1917 there was a definite westward as well as a deeper drilling trend in the developments. As the third decade closed the fields at Seminole and Oklahoma City were the centers of attention.

CHRONOLOGICAL TABLE
OF LOUISIANA OIL POOLS, 1915–30

Pool	Year Discovered	Parish and Region
Pine Island	1917–1918	Caddo, northwest
Homer	1919	Claiborne, north
Haynesville	1919	Claiborne, north
Bellevue	1921	Bossier, north
Cotton Valley	1922	Webster, north
Lockport	1924	Calcasieu, Gulf Coast
Rodessa (gas)	1926	Caddo, northwest
(oil)	1930	
Zwolle	1928	Sabine, north

Although Oklahoma and Texas led in the discovery of remarkable oil fields and the struggle with the problems of their administration, the history of the industry in Louisiana went through an almost identical development. In 1916 Louisiana's output amounted to more than fifteen million barrels of oil, valued at more than fifteen million dollars, placing the state in the fifth position in the national rating. Exploratory wells were drilled in five parishes in 1917, but the total output of the state declined so that it ranked sixth. As the soldiers of the United States crossed the Atlantic in 1918, the oil industry felt a growing demand at a rising price. When the higher price was felt in Louisiana, the oil producers set more rigs to work to increase the number of wells and the amount of crude oil. At the Pine Island Pool of Caddo Parish a great overproduction resulted in 1918 from the inadequacy of the transportation facilities. When the First World War ended, the main interest of the oil industry in Louisiana was held by the hundreds of large wells in Caddo Parish and the newly discovered pool in Claiborne Parish, both districts in the northern part of the state.

There were fifteen refineries with a daily treating capacity of one hundred thousand barrels of oil in Louisiana in 1919 when W. H. Rowe of Shreveport completed an immense gusher at Homer in Claiborne Parish. That was not the first well in the Homer Pool, but it was of such great capacity that at once a hasty rush for leases began. The drilling at the Homer Pool was far more costly than at most places, for there were no roads and the terrain was inclined to be swampy. Because casing and pipe from the legitimate dealers were very expensive, a large amount was "bootlegged" to the new field. The weather was wet, and at times cold, which added to the discomfort and difficulties of the workers. The makeshift roads became impassable, and there were instances when teams were mired so deep that they suffocated before they could be extricated. The excessive cost of transporting supplies often amounted to more than the sales price. It was not uncommon for a teamster to haul only two joints of pipe at one time, so difficult were the roads. Horses and mules were abandoned for oxen, which were more satisfactory because of the steadiness of their pulling. For the first time in the oil industry of that region, caterpillar tractors were used for hauling supplies. Two caterpillars were used to take a group of New York investors and oil company executives to inspect the pool.

As more wells were drilled the roads to the pool were improved, which in turn resulted in an increased number of holes. Few of the Homer Pool wells were permitted to flow

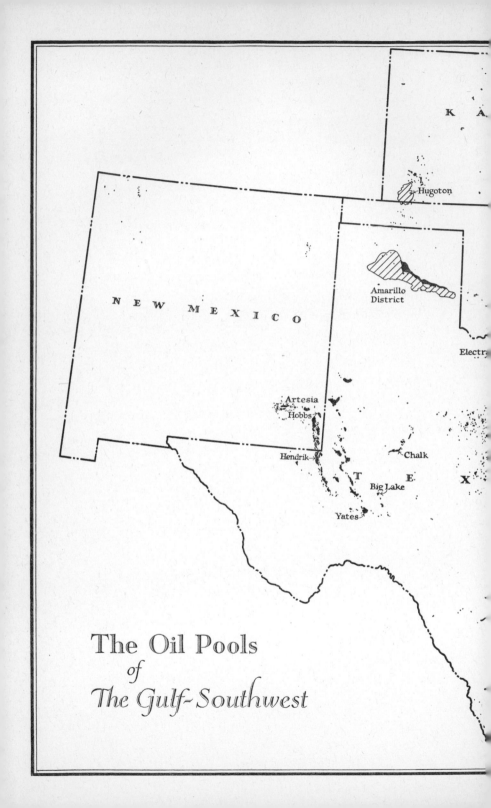

K A

Hugoton

Amarillo
District

NEW MEXICO

Electr

Artesia
Hobbs

Hendrik→

Chalk

T   E   X

Big Lake

Yates

The Oil Pools
of
The Gulf-Southwest

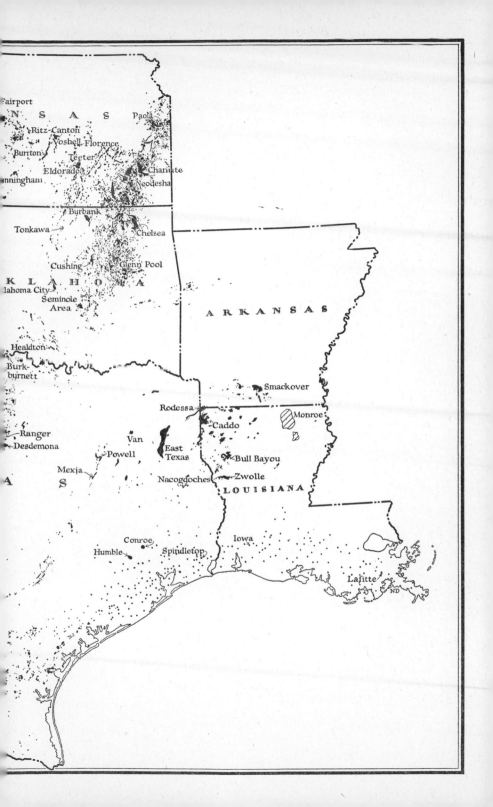

wide open, as there were no pipe lines and storage was limited. Many of the wells would have produced from twenty to thirty-five thousand barrels of oil, but most of them were pinched to fifteen thousand barrels or less. Most of the land was owned by Negroes, scores of whom became rich.

More fields of varying significance were discovered as the years passed, and the oil production of the state steadily increased until 1922, when it reached twenty million barrels. Pools had been found in Bossier, Ouachita, Morehouse, and Webster parishes. As the output of the Homer wells declined, deep and expensive production was found at the Cotton Valley Pool, and near Haynesville an area also was developed. The Cotton Valley wells were so deep as to delay development of the field. A sensational pool was discovered at Bellevue in 1921, wells less than four hundred feet deep yielding two thousand barrels a day. In Caddo Parish a well producing twenty-five thousand barrels of oil caught fire and burned for three weeks, although fifty boilers were used in an attempt to extinguish the flame with steam. Finally the fire was put out by diverting the oil.

The Louisiana oil producers were faced with new engineering problems in 1924 when the Lockport Pool was discovered on the Gulf Coast. It was in what was known as the Lockport Marsh, an area that consisted of about sixty feet of ooze coated with a few feet of coarse swamp grass. The roots of the grass formed a semifloating carpet, which was quite strong if unbroken. Occasionally a high tide covered the surface with water. To overcome these difficulties the operators constructed great roads on strong timbers with wide wooden foundations of heavy lumber. The roads in some cases were six feet high, although there were satisfactory thoroughfares made of shell. Some of the companies avoided the construction of roads by cutting canals through the swamp grass, but the dredging of water-ways was a very slow and expensive program. The use of canals involved another handicap: oil-field equipment was awkward to handle on barges. Altogether, millions of dollars were expended by oil companies in constructing roads, trestles, bridges, and canals.

The Gulf Coast was only one of the difficult regions in Louisiana that brought hardships to the oil producers. In the northwest, at the opposite end of the state, surface water was the basis of the troubles. There a drift of trees and logs from fifty to one hundred miles in length had cut off a large low area from the Red River. The river had flooded the land back of the "Great Raft," but it had not drained. Several long, shallow lakes resulted. By 1924 the most prolific lease in Caddo Parish was entirely submerged by the shallow water of a lake.

More than fifteen years of exploratory drilling, with an expenditure exceeding a million dollars, ended in the discovery in 1928 of the prolific Zwolle Pool, near the little town that once had been important in the Louisiana lumber industry. Walter E. Cook, of Paterson, New Jersey, had spent $650,000. Unsuccessful wells failed to cause Cook's withdrawal; instead he entered into partnership with two other men and leased thirty thousand acres of land. In 1928 petroleum was found at a little more than two thousand feet. Other wells followed, and in the autumn of 1929 one well rewarded its owners with a yield of more than fifteen thousand barrels of oil daily.

The drilling of wildcat wells in the Rodessa area of the northwest corner of Louisiana started in 1926, but shallow holes failed to find oil. Several deep wells that produced a large amount of gas were drilled. Then oil was struck at Rodessa, bringing legal production problems that involved both Texas and Arkansas also when the pool was extended into those two states. The third decade closed with geophysical methods responsible for the discovery of the Starks, Iberia, Hackberry, and Sulphur pools on the Gulf Coast. A vast amount of carbon black was manufactured in Louisiana, although it was slightly decreasing in quantity. Despite the fact that more dry holes than producers were drilled in 1930, there were 5,216 men employed in the operation of oil and gas wells. The refineries of the state gave work to 3,448 men.

While in Louisiana marine drilling and geophysical exploration became important, great strides were taken by the oil industry in Arkansas during the second fifteen years of the century. By 1917, exploratory wells were being drilled in fifteen counties of Arkansas, and in 1919 the initial hole was started in Ouachita County. That well, near Stephens, was completed at a little more than two thousand feet in 1920, with gas and a showing of oil, but it never became a commercial producer. Across the line in Union County another well was completed soon afterward with a production of sixty million cubic feet of natural gas and some oil. These wells, the preamble of the El Dorado Field, attracted such attention that during the year more than one hundred wells were started. At least two million dollars were paid for leases on twenty-one thousand acres in three counties in 1920.

Another stirring oil boom had started. The great El Dorado Pool became the incarnation of all the characteristics of other southwestern oil excitements. It was in a most inaccessible region of timber and poor roads. There was enough rain to make the roads impassable for long periods. The close of 1921 saw a field with five hundred wells, many of them flowing wild, where the discovery hole had been financed locally. The excitement had become intense in 1921 when a well in Union County had been completed with an initial flow of 7,500 barrels of oil and thirty thousand cubic feet of gas. That year, the state's first as an oil producer, Arkansas yielded ten million barrels of oil, the best initial year of any commonwealth.

An even more astonishing flush field was discovered in 1922 when in April a great gas well blew wild and cratered. The crater increased until it was 450 feet wide and 50 feet deep. That gas well marked the opening of the Smackover Pool, which included parts of both Ouachita and Union counties. Smackover became famous for the great initial production of its wells, many of them yielding from five thousand to ten thousand barrels, and one well, thirty thousand. The first oil well there was completed in July, and by the end of the year the daily production of the pool was ninety thousand barrels. A great amount of petroleum was placed in earthen storage, where because of evaporation it deteriorated rapidly. The Smackover oil was shipped to refineries at the rate of 72,500 barrels daily, but before the year came to a close it was estimated that 2,500,000 barrels had accumulated in storage. An odd characteristic of this field was the fact that it produced both light and heavy oils.

By 1924 the Smackover Pool contained more than one thousand wells with a production reaching one hundred thousand barrels a day; moreover, Arkansas rose to fourth rank among the oil-producing states. The next year Smackover became the leading oil field of the United States, when the third and fourth petroleum-bearing horizons were discovered. The average daily production approached two hundred thousand barrels, while during the year one oil-bearing formation alone yielded four hundred thousand barrels. Arkansas was at the height of its production in 1925 with a total of 77,398,000 barrels; the output generally declined until 1931.

Flush Production

CHRONOLOGICAL TABLE
OF KANSAS OIL POOLS, 1915–30

Pool	Year Discovered	County and Region
Eldorado	1917	Butler, central
Rainbow Bend	1923	Cowley, west
Gorham	1926	Russell, west
Ritz-Canton	1929	McPherson, west
Voshell	1929	McPherson, west
Hugoton (gas)	1930	Stevens, west

Just as the high war prices stimulated the oil industry in the discovery of new fields in other southwestern states, so during the second fifteen years of the century the western part of Kansas became an important source of petroleum. There was a great increase in the yield of the state in 1917 when the Trapshooters Oil Company drilled near Eldorado. That well flowed at a rate of about twenty thousand barrels a day and opened an important new pool. The state produced nearly 11 per cent of the nation's oil in 1917, and a record number of 3,474 wells were drilled in 1918. Not many of the Kansas pools were troubled with surface waste, because the oil was not accompanied by strong gas pressure that made control difficult.

While the state's yield declined and windmills were used to pump some of the shallow wells of the early eastern fields, commercial production was discovered in 1923 at Fairport in western Kansas. The well was a good one, but, as it was 125 miles from other oil pools, little development followed. In a year a pipe line was available to transport the oil and more holes were drilled. This pool was especially important because it led to the exploration of the western part of Kansas and the finding of other pools.

A large number of wildcats in western Kansas resulted in the opening of pools at Welch, Rainbow Bend, and Gorham. By the end of 1927 the new fields had produced more

80

than five million barrels of petroleum. Commercial oil deposits had been found in Russell, Rice, Reno, Rooks, Sumner, and Kingman counties. Subsurface information was being sought through the use of geophysics and the core drill, which in turn were encouraging more exploratory work. The large companies busily leased great blocks of land, a condition that tended to prevent the production of oil in excess of proper transportation facilities. The best discovery of 1928 was the Wright Pool near Wichita. In 1929 the operators at the bounteous Ritz-Canton Pool in McPherson County agreed to limit the production of their wells to one-half capacity, marking the beginning of proration in Kansas. In 1930 there were 4,512 men operating oil and gas wells in Kansas, the refineries of the state employed 1,147, and the pipe lines hired 852. The most far-reaching event of 1930 was the development of the great Hugoton gas region in western Kansas.

During the years that the oil industry was moving westward in Kansas, it became a leading industry in New Mexico, where in 1917 wildcat wells were drilled near Lamy, Almagordo, and Roswell. The study of southeastern New Mexico was redoubled after the discovery of the oil pools in near-by Winkler County, Texas. By 1919 the major companies had leased most of the territory between Carlsbad and Clayton, the legislature having provided for the letting of state land for oil. Exploratory wells were drilled that year near the towns of Portales, Carlsbad, Clovis, Tucumcari, and Clayton. In the San Juan River basin in northwestern New Mexico, leases in 1922 amounted to 150,000 acres. The land was owned by the Navajo Indians and the Federal government, and in 1923 the first lease sale was held at Santa Fé. The next year, an output of ninety-eight thousand barrels was recorded for the Hogback Pool of San Juan County and a pipe line had been arranged to a loading rack at Farmington. The Rattlesnake Dome Pool came later, and a pipe line was constructed to Gallup.

The first significant well in southeastern New Mexico was drilled near Artesia in 1923. It produced gas at the rate of 1,500,000 cubic feet daily, and the enthusiastic chamber of commerce at Roswell, about fifty miles to the north, offered a bonus of twenty-five thousand dollars to the driller of the first well within thirty miles of that city. Geophysical crews were set to work exploring the western side of the great Permian Basin, in which large pools had been found in Texas. More than two million cubic feet of gas from Artesia was being consumed in 1925 by the towns of the Pecos River Valley. There were 135 wells in the Artesia gas-producing area when the first productive well in Lea County was drilled in 1925. This hole, near Jal, produced ninety million cubic feet of gas. More drilling followed, and a producing horizon was developed in 1928 at little more than four thousand feet, near the country store and schoolhouse known as Hobbs.

The first important New Mexico oil was discovered at Hobbs in 1929 when the Bowers No. 1 produced nearly ten thousand barrels of petroleum. Immediately an active drilling campaign took place, and a flood of petroleum followed. Only a limited market was available, a condition that caused the operators of the pool to agree to co-operative development. The legislature legalized this co-ordinated proration agreement, and in 1930 a committee of operators took charge of the Hobbs Field, where there were only twenty-one companies. Hobbs was transformed into a city of twelve thousand, the second largest in New Mexico. Two gasoline extraction plants were erected to treat the gas, and pipe lines were extended from West Texas to take the oil to refineries. Lovington, the seat of the Lea County government, was supplied with natural gas, and geophysical crews explored and examined the region in all directions searching for more petroleum.

The southwestern petroleum industry became a vital part of the national economic life between 1915 and 1930, a period of exploration and discovery throughout these six oil-producing states. For many uses, oil displaced coal. The effect of the first World War was felt by the oil industry in 1916 when a shortage of drilling tools and casing became apparent. The prices were higher and delivery was slower because of the conflict. The war also increased railway traffic; consequently the demand for fuel grew as thirty-two roads consumed more than forty-five million barrels of oil in 1917. The Allies were said to have "floated to victory on a sea of oil," because of increased mechanization.

From the thousands of wells of the Southwest more than twenty-eight million barrels of oil were placed in storage in 1917, and consumption continued to increase. The growing demand was met and stabilized by the oil taken from storage, so that the average price for the year remained about $1.50 a barrel. The output of the Southwest was augmented through great effort on the part of the producers, but the demand still swelled. A great deal of petroleum was sent from the United States to the warring nations in Europe, and submarines took a toll of the tankers. As the Federal government assumed control of essential industries, leading oil men formed the National Petroleum War Service Committee and set up an organization that offered to assist in the administration.

The whole industry was placed under the guidance of the United States Fuel Administration in 1918, the year that the Texas Gulf Coast and Louisiana Oil Producers Association was formed. The coastal operators organized themselves because the laborers had united and struck for increased wages. The situation had become more pressing when manufacturers raised the prices of materials. The operators finally appealed to the Federal government to fix the price of crude oil at a profitable level. Under the Fuel Administration higher rates were paid, and conditions gradually improved.

The output of the southwestern states increased in 1919 to more than 216,000,000 barrels of oil, valued at more than $445,000,000. The American Petroleum Institute, representing the financial interests in the industry, was organized in 1919 with the 2,800 members of the National Petroleum War Service Committee as a basis. Between 1915 and 1922 more than 4,900 oil companies had been formed and authorized to issue stock amounting to $8,-967,477,000. In the first ten months of 1920 more than fifteen hundred new companies were formed. Because fear was expressed that the deposits of oil soon would be exhausted, plans for mining petroleum were suggested. In 1921 prices rose to the highest level in the history of the industry, except for the first few years when Kansas and Oklahoma crude was sold at the wells for three dollars a barrel. Retail prices of gasoline approached thirty cents a gallon, and the cry was heard for economy in use, additional exploration, and efficiency in production.

The depression of 1921 and 1922 failed to reduce the production of petroleum in the Southwest, for the output of the second of these years approached 350,000,000 barrels. The five states of Oklahoma, Texas, Arkansas, Kansas, and Louisiana contained more than ninety-five thousand wells, over the production of which only slight control was exercised. The demand for petroleum constantly increased, and by 1922 oil was the fuel burned on 3,110 American ships. By 1924 there were almost one hundred thousand oil wells in the Southwest, and these yielded more than half of the national output.

Petroleum in Abundance

The public began to read a new theory of petroleum production in 1926 when the spokesmen of the major companies issued statements calling attention to the desirability of proration and conservation. The American Petroleum Institute issued a booklet that was circulated widely to show that there was a plentiful supply of oil and that no control of production was needed. The prices were high and most profitable. Then the prolific Seminole and Yates pools were discovered, causing the price of crude oil to drop while the large companies had their storage tanks filled with petroleum purchased at peak rates. It was then that the main organizations, all of which were members of the American Petroleum Institute, realized that production should be limited. Attention was called to physical waste, and also to the much broader term, subject to many interpretations, *economic waste*. The need to conserve the natural resources through limiting the production of the different fields was emphasized.

By 1928 the oil-producing states of the country were being urged to unite in a legal movement to reduce their production. The Southwest would be most affected by such a movement, for in those six states more than six hundred million barrels of oil came from the ground. Oklahoma and Texas together were yielding more petroleum than the three leading foreign nations of Venezuela, Russia, and Mexico. A meeting of oil company executives was held at Colorado Springs in June, 1929, to plan interstate co-operation by which production could be reduced. The meeting soon was divided by the conflicting interests of the larger companies, with international holdings, and the so-called independents, whose properties were all in the United States.

The big firms wished to arrange a plan, through an interstate agreement, by which domestic production could be reduced. The independent companies refused to adhere to

85

any such program so long as their giant rivals remained free to import crude oil from their wells in Mexico or Venezuela. While the large concerns did not lose sight of their intention to carry through the Interstate Oil Compact, the Independent Petroleum Association of America established headquarters at Washington in 1930 and sought a tariff on oil. The independents went so far as to accuse the major companies of responsibility for excess production and low prices through the importation of petroleum for refining and marketing. A remarkably powerful lobby worked in Washington for the tariff, the first time that such governmental interference in the oil industry had been sought.

The third decade of the century closed with important events transpiring in the various states as well as at Washington. In New Mexico the Hobbs Pool was developing with unusual rapidity. The East Texas Field was reaching proportions that attracted national attention. In Kansas the immense Hugoton gas area was being developed to supply the cities of Chicago, Omaha, and Saint Louis with fuel. Two Oklahoma fields, Seminole and Oklahoma City, were the centers of interest in that state. The flush production of these great oil pools had set on foot two highly significant movements. The independent companies were seeking a tariff that would protect their domestic interests from the foreign oil of their larger competitors, while an effort to prevent Federal control of the industry was being made through the promotion of the Interstate Oil Compact.

The Era of Regulation

THE rugged selfishness that characterized the oil industry during the first thirty years of this century found itself facing bankruptcy when the fourth decade began. Great integrated companies, with holdings of wells, pipe lines, refineries, and retail outlets, owned millions of barrels of oil in storage—and countless more could be purchased at a few cents a barrel. The complex refineries of these companies were affected by the reduced consumption that hindered the entire nation during panic years of the depression. Some of the small plants, however, had local markets, which in a few cases even expanded at the expense of the larger companies. The producers also were injured by the rapid decline in the price of crude oil. Some of them, who had previously operated their properties at a profit, were forced to borrow thousands of dollars just to keep their wells open. The situation at the opening of the fourth decade called for decisive action affecting the oil industry of the Gulf-Southwest.

The disturbing center of interest in the region was the East Texas Pool, where early in 1931 the wells presented a picture of the possible size of the producing area. At once the Texas Railroad Commission began issuing restrictive regulations. The producers responded with injunctions that obstructed the enforcement of the rules. Since some of the wells were permitted to flow at full capacity, the drilling of offsets, which took as much oil as their neighbors, was allowed. Some of the big wells did not have pipe-line connections for transporting their output to market, so it went into storage. Early in the development of the pool the petroleum often was sold at twenty-five cents a barrel, but as the yield increased and the producing area grew, the price dropped. Some of the smaller owners sold their oil at five and ten cents a barrel to induce pipe-line connections.

Conditions became chaotic. Thousands of laborers, teamsters with their horses and mules, hundreds of trucks and their operators, all congested the roads through the pine trees of the growing East Texas Field. The Railroad Commission failed to restrain the drilling of more wells, with the result that eight months after the Joiner discovery hundreds were producing. Temporary living quarters of every sort and description appeared on all sides, as in great haste wells were drilled, pipe lines laid, and refineries constructed. By August, 1931, more than sixteen hundred wells were producing daily in excess of one million barrels of petroleum, in a field that was thirty-two miles long and about three miles wide.

The major companies, although their officials denounced overproduction, were as busy obtaining oil as the small firms, a condition resulting from the great number of small landholdings. Tank trucks, employed by the small local refiners, hauled the low-priced gasoline to retail outlets for miles in every direction. The national gasoline market was disrupted and disorganized by the millions of gallons from the dozens of small refineries that were operating in the district. About the middle of August, Governor Ross Sterling, a wealthy oil man himself, proclaimed martial law in the East Texas area. Production was stopped when the pool was placed in the control of the militia. For three weeks, while information on local conditions and on the market was collected, the militia kept operations closed. It was argued that too many wells had been drilled in the pool, and the town of Kilgore was cited as a pepperbox example. In Kilgore several hundred wells were drilled, as many as three being placed on single lots in some cases. With the declaration of martial law, the operators in the pool were quickly separated by their economic interests into two antagonistic camps: the independents, whose holdings generally were confined to that one pool, and the majors, whose properties were national or international. The independents, despite the remarkably low price of oil, insisted on opening their wells to capacity production. They were joined by the small refiners, who could get a plentiful supply of cheap crude oil through a flush yield. The big companies, owners of millions of barrels of oil in storage, wanted a stringent reduction of the East Texas output.

When the field was reopened, the Texas Railroad Commission ordered all wells choked to a daily flow of 225 barrels. Then more wells were drilled. Additional pipe lines to transport the petroleum were constructed. By December there were 3,600 producing wells, and 1,000 others were being drilled. Eighteen pipe lines took the petroleum from the pool, which contained more than fifteen hundred miles of trunk lines. Major companies bought the holdings of many small operators, but the rapid drilling and producing continued unabated. With the legal allowable fixed at 225 barrels a well, the small refineries should have found the supply of crude limited, but they continued to operate at capacity. Then it became known that many wells were producing in excess of their allowables. That was "hot," or illegal, oil. Though it was known to exist, "hot oil" was most difficult to discover. It could be taken from the wells through concealed pipes, for instance. It could be piped around gauges and cutoffs. Official gaugers could be in-

duced to misread the meters, and some operators considered such violations of the law legitimate.

During the rapid development of the pool by hundreds
of firms with limited finances, a great quantity of old and
used material and machinery was used. There were dozens
of fires, some of which resulted directly from the use of
faulty materials. Twelve persons lost their lives in two of
the fires, and one well continued to burn for twenty-six
days before the flames were extinguished. Many accidents
resulted from the use of millions of tons of worn equipment.
Steel storage tanks for seven million barrels of petroleum
were erected. In no similar area of the world had so many
refineries and pipe lines been constructed in a year as were
in East Texas in 1931. Nor had so many little shack towns
been built as in this area.

The illegal output of the East Texas Field was reduced
in 1932, when the producing region was thirty-five miles
long and from three to nine miles wide. It was recognized
as the leading oil district of the world. The legal daily production of a well was reduced during the year to fifty-nine
barrels, which caused the drilling of more holes instead of
the intended curtailment of output. In that one year the
pool produced more petroleum than had been taken from
Spindletop in thirty-one years. The illegal output of the
area was never recorded. In 1933 there were 11,600 wells
in the East Texas Pool, and more were being drilled. The
condition of the market had grown steadily worse during
1932, with millions of gallons of gasoline being made available for consumption. At a meeting at Fort Worth the Texas
Independent Refiners Association, representing seventy
plants with a total daily capacity of two hundred thousand
barrels, was formed. The board of directors of the organization wrote a code for their industry which was put into
effect by the National Industrial Recovery Administration.

The illegally produced oil was barred from interstate commerce by the Federal government, which in September stopped five hundred cars of petroleum. The Federal government attempted to restrict production to consumer demand, thereby justifying a price of one dollar a barrel for crude petroleum.

Continued drilling during the depressed days of 1933 increased the length of the East Texas Pool to fifty miles. The wells generally cost about twenty thousand dollars to complete and equip, a figure that would be paid out by a well in forty or fifty months. The district was equal to one-fourth of the total area of the forty largest pools that had been discovered in the United States before 1931. It alone was capable of supplying the needs of the nation for three years. The high gasoline content of the crude oil was paralleled by the value of the gas of the pool, which contained from four to six gallons for each thousand cubic feet. With more wells being drilled every month, as potential production increased and prices dropped, the rig-builders succeeded in shutting down new operations throughout the field when they struck and gained a raise of two dollars a day in their wages. The effect of the growing number of wells was also felt throughout the pool in June, 1934, when the reservoir pressure fell sharply. Estimates placed the daily production of the region at more than five hundred thousand, of which one-fifth was "hot oil."

The burden of cheap petroleum placed on the national market by East Texas became the subject of an attack on the industry. Harold L. Ickes, Secretary of the Department of the Interior, who had become Federal administrator of the oil industry under the National Industrial Recovery Act, addressed the American Petroleum Institute at Dallas in November, 1934. He emphatically denounced the minority in the East Texas Pool who were producing oil illegally.

He called attention to the condition of the industry before he had participated in its operation, and then cited the profits that had been made during the operation of the N.R.A. code. His listeners were angered when Ickes, contending that government control was desirable, asked, "How did it happen that the oil industry got into such a mess and why did it ever think of appealing to the Government for help?" Ickes suggested that the rugged self-interest of the men in the industry should be curbed by the Federal government.

Five counties contained parts of the vast East Texas Pool by 1935. That year the oil companies began to operate somewhat as a unit, despite the fact that the N.R.A. code ceased functioning. The rate of production for each well, however, was fixed by officials who in some cases were accused of selling high potential ratings. The state of Texas found itself in the oil business also, as a result of the accumulation of confiscated petroleum. Some operators even attempted to profit by producing oil illegally and then buying it from the state after it had been confiscated.

Twenty-nine major companies owned 10,410 of the East Texas wells in 1935, and more than one thousand small firms owned over twelve thousand wells. The large number of companies and the variation of their interests made a common administrative policy for the pool a virtual impossibility. The Connally "Hot Oil" Act, prohibiting the shipment of illegally produced petroleum in interstate commerce, became effective in 1935 after the United States Supreme Court had nullified the National Industrial Recovery Act. The Department of Justice opened a branch office at Tyler, Texas, which instituted 222 criminal prosecutions in 1936. By 1937 a total of 248 Federal cases had been filed, with the government gaining convictions in 231. Four Federal courts upheld the Connally Act in 1937.

The Era of Regulation

About fifty new wells were completed each week in 1937, but difficult physical problems developed in the East Texas Field. Chief among the problems were those of water encroachment and falling reservoir pressure. About four thousand wells were producing salt water at a rate of seventy-five thousand barrels daily. Production of water reduced the pressure of the pool as rapidly as the removal of the oil, for in some cases immense amounts of liquid were taken from the wells in order to get only a few barrels of petroleum. By 1937 the spacing of the wells in the field averaged less than six acres to a well, and when the year began three thousand of the wells were being pumped. The wells had flowed about 30 per cent of the ultimate yield of the pool, making the preservation of the reservoir energy pressingly important. Some of the wells were plugged back to shut off the water, in many cases by the newly developed technique of squeeze cementing (plugging back with cement under extremely high pressure). The disposal of the salt water had become a serious problem for the producers. Several plans were used, the most common being the construction of earthen tanks where the water was held for evaporation. Operators were most eager to delay the time when all the wells would become pumpers, thereby increasing the cost of the petroleum.

The East Texas Pool was producing more than two hundred million barrels of petroleum annually in 1937 when arrangements were made to close the area on Sundays. Eight hundred wells were exempted from the shutdown to supply fuel for the residents of the area. The owners of the wells in the water-producing part of the pool feared that their properties would be ruined by increased encroachment if shut down. The twenty natural gasoline plants in the field were also closed, and the pipe lines emptied the storage tanks on the leases during the inactive days. Four idle Sun-

93

Flush Production

days reduced the production of the pool to the demand estimate of the United States Bureau of Mines.

An indication of the economic conditions in the East Texas Pool in 1938 is given by the fact that it was possible to buy a barrel of gasoline there for $1.47, while the crude oil itself sold for $1.40. To the small refiners with local markets that condition was ruinous. The natural pressure had fallen to a point that forced 37 per cent of the wells to be pumped.

The United States Department of Justice investigated conditions in the pool, charging some officials and major companies with violating the antitrust laws in fixing prices. Several convictions were returned by the Federal court at Madison, Wisconsin.

Seven years after its discovery the East Texas Pool covered an area of more than 130,000 acres in parts of five

CHRONOLOGICAL TABLE
OF TEXAS OIL POOLS, 1930–40

Pool	Year Discovered	County and Region
K-M-A (deep)	1931	Wichita, north
Conroe	1931	Montague, Gulf Coast
Tomball	1933	Harris & Montgomery, Gulf Coast
Ace	1933	Polk, Gulf Coast
Louise	1933	Wharton, Gulf Coast
Cleveland	1933	Liberty, Gulf Coast
Long Lake	1934	Anderson, east central
Cayuga	1934	Anderson, east central
Splendora	1934	Montgomery, Gulf Coast
Van Vleck	1934	Matagorda, Gulf Coast
Rodessa	1935	Cass & Marion, northeast
Anahuac	1935	Chambers, Gulf Coast
Fairbanks	1938	Harris, Gulf Coast
Cedar Point	1938	Chambers, Gulf Coast

counties and had broken most of the records in the oil industry. Its potential hourly production was estimated at 14,863,792 barrels. The waste in the drilling of thousands of unnecessary wells in the development of the field was variously fixed at $80,000,000 to $160,000,000. Some believed that the immense reservoir could have been drained adequately with less than seven thousand wells—instead of nearly four times that number, as was actually the case. The ultimate recovery of petroleum from the East Texas Pool was expected to mount into billions of barrels.

Although the principal interest of the oil industry in the state was in East Texas, the operators in other sections were not idle. In Wichita County, where national interest had been attracted during the Burkburnett hysteria, the K-M-A Pool was again the center of a boom, this time affecting leases on one hundred thousand acres of land.

More important, however, was the discovery of the Conroe Pool in the inner Gulf Coast region near Houston. George Choate, of Houston, had developed an electrical apparatus with which he had studied the Conroe district, and in 1925 he had predicted a large oil deposit. He had leased more than four thousand acres of land, but had not succeeded in promoting a well. In 1927 he had tried and failed again. The discovery well was drilled by George W. Strake in 1931, bringing more flush production to a state already burdened with too much oil. Although Conroe was a major field it was additionally important because it attracted the industry to an area that had previously been avoided. It called the attention of oil men to a thirty-five-mile zone about nine hundred miles long, lying seventy-five miles inland. Leasing throughout this zone resulted from the Conroe Pool in 1932.

One of the outstanding wild wells of all time was drilled there in 1933 when a hole that subsequently produced six thousand barrels of petroleum daily blew out of control. The great gas pressure caused the well to crater, necessitating fire prevention efforts. Thirty-six watchmen were employed to prevent trespassing while a crew drilled a relief well. A battery of boilers kept the great crater covered with live steam. No matches were permitted near the well. Equipment was erected that was capable of covering the crater with twelve inches of foam in eleven minutes in case of fire. The uncontrolled production of the well was impounded and sold, and with directional drilling the flow was cut off by the new hole. From June, 1933, to January, 1934, the wild well produced more than 1,225,000 barrels of petroleum. It was not subject to proration, because the crater was deemed an act of God. The Conroe Pool in later years became a model in development and operation.

In Bosque County, where the land was quite valuable for agriculture, windmills were installed to pump the wells of a shallow pool so that the land could be tilled. After seismic examination, a large block of leases was arranged in Anderson County, and in 1934 the discovery well of the Cayuga Pool was drilled. It initially produced six thousand barrels of oil.

On the Gulf Coast of Texas several more pools were discovered, and in 1934 the "poor boys" were particularly energetic in the southwestern part of the state. Petroleum here was found in many instances at depths of less than a thousand feet, and most inexpensive equipment could make such holes. The motors of discarded automobiles were used to supply power for the rigs. Some of the wells in Zapata County were as shallow as 160 feet; in Refugio County they approached 7,000 feet. In San Patricio County the gas-oil ratio of some pools was too high for the rules of Texas, a condition especially characteristic of "condensate" wells. Other wells produced ninety barrels of brine for each ten of petroleum. At the Government Wells Pool in Duval County, wells that would flow at the rate of one hundred barrels an hour were choked by proration to forty-five barrels a day, and a similar situation existed in most Texas fields. In this particular district a hole could be drilled in fifteen days for ten thousand dollars or less, because of the soft formations. In the Edwards Plateau area near San Antonio, more time and money were necessary. The most difficult drilling in southwestern Texas was in the lower coastal district where the wells were six thousand or more feet deep, the gas pressures were tremendous, and the bits had to pass through a heaving shale formation. All sorts of engineering devices and scientific skills were required in different parts of the great territory. The region included sixty counties with more than 150 oil fields. In some areas, oil was expected to be found as deep as it was possible to drill. Fifty-five pools were discovered in six months of 1937. Between 1921—when the area first became important for its oil—and 1940, Corpus Christi became an important refining and exporting city on the Gulf Coast.

A great coastal discovery was made in 1935 with the opening of the Anahuac Pool in Chambers County, where the Humble Oil and Refining Company held leases on twelve thousand acres. Eighty-one pools were producing oil on the Texas Gulf Coast in 1938, and more than two million acres of land, yet undeveloped, were held by leases. By 1940 an almost unbroken line of oil fields extended from the Rio Grande to the Mississippi River. In known reserves, the Gulf Coast outranked all other districts in the United States.

Partly as a result of the fact that immense quantities of petroleum were found near at hand, but chiefly because of the cheap marine transportation, the largest refining center in the world developed in the Beaumont–Port Arthur

97

district. There were six great refineries, one employing nine thousand men, with a total capacity of 422,000 barrels daily, nearly one-tenth of the processing of the United States. Twenty pipe lines poured petroleum into steel storage tanks of 50,518,517 barrels capacity. The monthly pay roll of the oil industry at Beaumont was more than $3,500,-000. The ports of Texas now contained berths for loading seventy tankers at a time.

Leasing in West Texas surpassed all previous years in 1937, with the result that the large companies acquired the oil rights on more than eight million acres in the Permian Basin. The Permian Basin was the bed of an ancient sea, eight hundred miles long and three hundred miles wide, extending from the Texas Panhandle toward the Rio Grande and including southeastern New Mexico. There were ninety-two oil pools containing 9,411 wells on 2,150 leases. Wells in the Permian Basin might cost more than forty thousand dollars to drill, whereas in northern Texas the shallow producing horizons were looked upon as the paradise of the independent producer because the holes were much cheaper. In the twenty-seven counties of northern Texas there were more than five hundred pools. In some of the wells acid and other systems were being used to revive the production.

Near Nacogdoches, one of the earliest oil-producing areas in Texas, the mining of petroleum was started in 1935. Good lubricating stock was found in the shale and sandstone 50 to 250 feet deep about fifteen miles southeast of Nacogdoches. The area was neglected for long periods between 1870 and 1935 because of the low gasoline and kerosene content. The method of mining was to open the raw surface of the horizon to permit the petroleum to seep to the bottom of the shaft, from which it was pumped.

The most notable event of 1935 was the extension of the Rodessa Pool from Caddo Parish, Louisiana, to Cass Coun-

*The old style wooden
drilling rig* . . .

MEYERS, OKLAHOMA CITY

. . . *has been superseded by steel construction*

OKLAHOMA GEOLOGICAL SURVEY

*Early type of spudding machine, used only for
shallow wells*

OIL & GAS JOURNAL

*A familiar scene during the rainy season at Seminole in the
early days of its oil production*

ty, Texas. The Rodessa Pool was first regarded as only a
gas-producing area. Wells had been drilled there sporadi-
cally since 1910, but the first oil well in Texas in that area
was drilled in 1935. The crude petroleum had a satisfactory
gasoline content, but the drilling was slow and difficult.
Twenty to thirty rock bits were required during the seventy-
five days necessary to drill one of the Rodessa wells. The
nearest pipe line was eight miles away, but the railroads and
highways were nearer. The second well produced at the rate
of five hundred barrels hourly. By the end of the year geologists and geophysicists had traced the oil-bearing formation into Arkansas as well as Texas and Louisiana, and development was expected in that state.

Early in 1936 the producers of the East Texas Pool were
objecting to the Rodessa development, for from the newer
flush area petroleum was being shipped which competed
with theirs. They argued that if the Connally Act protected
the rest of the country from the cheap oil of East Texas,
something should be done to protect East Texas from Rodessa. A pipe line was laid from Rodessa to a refinery at
Longview, Texas, which increased their displeasure. When
seventy wells had been completed in the area, it was estimated that eventually the pool would cover twenty-seven
thousand acres and that the ultimate recovery would be
more than two hundred million barrels. Such questions as
pressures, gas-oil ratios, water encroachments, and porosity
of the formation were being studied by scientists. Meanwhile the drilling time had been reduced to about forty days.

Governmental control of the pool was complicated by the
fact that the area extended into three states. On the Louisiana side of the pool gas was wasted at the rate of about six
hundred million cubic feet daily. There the average well
had a ratio of one barrel of oil to ten thousand cubic feet
of gas. The rapid extraction of this gas resulted in reduc-

ing the pressure of the entire reservoir. Texas operators were especially annoyed by the fact that the Louisiana wells were permitted to produce far more oil than their own were, so the Texas Railroad Commission fixed allowables equal to those in the adjoining state.

In April, 1936, there were 120 wells in the Rodessa Pool, which had produced more than four million barrels of petroleum from 6,500 acres. The next month one company gained special permission to open its wells to full capacity despite the allowable of 350 barrels a well. In June all the two hundred wells in both states were reduced to 275 barrels a day, while on the Louisiana side twenty-two wells were beginning to produce salt water. In 1936 the Louisiana section of the pool alone produced nineteen million barrels of oil, which was nearly double the total yield of the entire state for the previous year.

By 1938 this field was thirty-five miles long and more than four miles wide, and contained more than one thousand wells. It had produced nearly eighty-three million barrels of oil, of 43 degrees gravity and paraffin base. The reserve was estimated at more than 250,000,000 barrels. Two years later the field had been extended to cover parts of Caddo Parish, Louisiana; Marion and Cass counties, Texas; and Miller County, Arkansas. Its development had been characterized by intensive drilling, excessive gas-oil ratios, premature release of natural gas from solution and the consequent dissipation of reservoir energy.

The Rodessa Pool was but another producing area in the eastern part of Texas, the section of the state that for years had occupied a leading position in the oil industry. This part of Texas was credited with having had the state's first oil well, the first pool, the first pipe line, the first steel storage, the first commercial oil pool, and the first complete refinery. In this section the modern rotary rig was developed; petroleum was adapted to locomotives as fuel; and an attempt was made to burn gas as a locomotive fuel. And finally, the greatest oil pool in the history of the petroleum industry was discovered and developed here. The cumulative production of the pools in the eastern part of Texas by 1940 was about 1,500,000,000 barrels of petroleum.

New wells were being completed in Texas at the rate of about one an hour in 1940, and there had been 185,797 drilled in the previous fifty years. Of the total, 52,420 had been dry, a proportion of one duster to every three and one-half holes. Petroleum had been found in 144 counties of the state, and prospecting had been active in most of those remaining. Texas contained nearly one-fourth of the world's petroleum and about two-fifths of that of the United States.

CHRONOLOGICAL TABLE
OF LOUISIANA OIL POOLS, 1930–40

Pool	Year Discovered	Parish and Region
Rodessa	1930	Caddo, northwest
Lake Washington	1931	Plaquemines, Gulf Coast
Roanoke	1934	Jefferson Davis, Gulf Coast
Bosco	1934	Acadia & St. Landry, Gulf Coast
Lake Hermitage	1934	Plaquemines, Gulf Coast
Lisbon	1936	Claiborne & Lincoln, north
Creole	1938	Cameron, Gulf Coast

The Iowa Pool, in Calcasieu and Jefferson Davis parishes of Louisiana, demonstrated its copiousness in 1933 when seventeen wells produced nearly two million barrels of petroleum in ten months, in spite of chokes on the flow pipes. Two other pools on the Gulf Coast, Lake Hermitage and Lake Washington, required the use of marine drilling equipment. Such pools were often developed through the use of barges, which held the drilling rigs and quarters for the crews. In some cases the workers were transported by boat to land camps, while in others living accommodations were erected on pilings in the water. The water of the southern Louisiana lakes and bayous was affected by the tides, however, and the barges formed the most satisfactory bases for operation. Wells of eight or nine thousand barrels capacity were common.

The outstanding development in the Louisiana oil industry in 1935 was the drilling and production activity at the Rodessa Pool. Then in 1936 the Lisbon Pool of Claiborne and Lincoln parishes was discovered. Here the wells were drilled rapidly despite an average cost of forty thousand dollars. In two years the pool contained 173 wells and extended over four thousand acres; the operators expected that it would eventually cover twenty-five thousand. The Louisiana oil men were inclined to let their wells flow at a high rate. The state was not a member of the Interstate Oil Compact, hence the suggested allocations of the United States Bureau of Mines were not followed.

Fourteen new pools were discovered on the Louisiana Gulf Coast in 1937, making a total of sixty-one in that division of the state. Three of the new coastal pools were more than ten thousand feet deep, and there were indications that future drilling would penetrate even farther. Most of the deep holes were in southern Louisiana, which outranked all other parts of the world in this respect with its wells of more than ten thousand feet.

The Creole Pool, found off the coast of Cameron Parish in 1938, required drilling in fourteen feet of sea water. The ultimate recovery from this pool was expected to be more than two million barrels of oil. Thirty-two parishes of southern Louisiana were producing petroleum at the time, giving that district more than half of the state's reserves.

In northern Louisiana the Caddo Parish pools covered sixty thousand acres, much of which was below the surface of the broad but shallow Caddo Lake.

With the beginning of the fourth decade of this century, definite state control of the oil industry reached Kansas. In March, 1931, the legislature authorized the Public Service Commission to regulate production. The Kansas proration law was an expression of the effect of the depression on the industry, as well as an indication of increased production. Since the oil industry in Kansas was more than forty years old, a large number of the pools had dropped to the stripper classification; about one-third of the state's production came from such wells, many of which were in the southeastern part of the state. After 1931, the discovery of deeper sands, the development of geophysical exploration, and the increased use of acid to revive old pools resulted in a sharp increase in potential production.

One company, in Crawford County, consisting of a force of six men, carried out all phases of the industry in 1934 and 1935. In these two years they drilled thirty wells, which were pumped with electricity generated on the lease. The wells were about 225 feet deep, and from each one an average of two barrels of oil was taken each day. Power for the operations was derived from an automobile motor and a 2,300-volt generator. The cooling system consisted of two automobile radiators. The refinery included a forty-five-barrel shell still, a steam boiler, a refractionating tower, and a condenser. This company had a local market for its manufactured product.

Many small pools in Kansas were discovered in 1934, but the greatest year for successful wildcats was 1935, when fifty productive areas were found. In this same year the legislature approved the use of water-flooding to repressure oil pools. The Burrton Pool became an important flush area, and pipe lines were extended westward to connect with several shut-in new pools. More than sixty oil and gas reservoirs were discovered in 1936, and at the Oxford Pool one well was reported to have produced sixteen thousand barrels of oil in a day. By 1937 there were more than 150 oil fields in western Kansas. Among the counties containing several producing areas were Russell, which had thirty-seven pools; Barton, with sixteen; Rice, with twenty-six; and Ellis, with sixteen. The reserves of oil in western Kansas were difficult to estimate, because most of the discoveries had not been developed. Generally the pools were not drained until transportation facilities were available for moving the crude petroleum to a refinery. Most of the leases were owned by large companies that could delay production until desirable marketing conditions arose. The wells usually were from three to four thousand feet deep and from the beginning were limited in their flow. Sulphur was commonly found in the oil, which made it less desirable, but by 1938 Kansas had a daily potential production of three million barrels. Especially notable was the development of the gas industry after the discovery of the Hugoton Field in Southwestern Kansas. The Hugoton Field covered two thousand square miles of territory and was capable of yielding sixty billion cubic feet of gas. A large amount of its production was piped for consumption to the metropolitan areas of the Middle West.

By 1940 the proved reserves of Kansas had been estimated at more than 600,000,000 barrels, and the production was 175,000 barrels daily. In the southeastern part of the state there were 15,000 oil wells, most of them strippers, while the western part contained 250 pools, many of them undeveloped. In the fourth decade the oil industry in Kansas had definitely concentrated on the exploration and development of the twenty thousand square miles of territory that became known as "western Kansas," although much of it was in the state's geographical center.

When the fourth decade of the century opened, New Mexico had six refineries with a daily capacity of seven thousand barrels of petroleum. Transportation was through 350 miles of oil pipe line and 750 miles of trunk gas line. Three natural gasoline plants removed the liquid parts of fifty million cubic feet of gas daily. Little drilling was done in 1931 because of the low price of crude oil, and the state ranked sixth in its total production. Water encroachment became troublesome in 1932, and New Mexico's output continued to decline. The Artesia Pool was discovered in 1933, wells between two and three thousand feet deep encountering a producing horizon three hundred feet thick.

Although the Hobbs Pool yielded three-fourths of the state's production in 1934, the Jal area also became important and the Cooper and Monument pools were discovered. The Monument Pool was named for the large statue of a pointing Indian that stood near by, erected to guide thirsty persons to a water hole. The lack of water was one of the serious difficulties confronting the oil industry in New Mexico, as large amounts were required for drilling. Companies made a business of supplying water for drilling oil wells, charging a flat rate of two thousand dollars for a sixty-day supply for a rotary rig and half that amount for a diesel plant.

The production of the East Texas Pool had been stabilized by 1937, with a consequent increase in the demand for the West Texas–New Mexico output. Proration, which affected both Texas and New Mexico producers, had the effect of reducing the yield of each well and increasing the number of holes that were drilled. Six pipe lines took oil from the Permian Basin, but their capacity was not large enough to move the allowables of New Mexico. Five new pools were discovered in the state in 1938, three in Lea County and two in Eddy County, but the total production of the state still declined. By the close of the decade many New Mexico operators were facing the problem of lifting the oil from their wells. Natural pressure would raise the oil at a cost of three to five cents a barrel, while artificial methods brought this amount to about twenty-five cents. The gas, as a natural lifting medium, was highly important, but the formations were so porous that gas might move without forcing the petroleum along. By 1940 Lea County contained twenty-four pools and Eddy County eleven. Much of the oil had been discovered on land that the state and Federal governments had been unable to sell, and which, of course, now became profitable to them. Only 38 per cent of the New Mexico oil land was privately owned: 42 per cent was the property of New Mexico, and the United States owned the remaining one-fifth.

At the start of the fourth decade, the average price of crude oil in Arkansas was less than fifty cents a barrel. The total yield for 1931 was less than fifteen million barrels. Although the search for additional pools continued, the production of the state declined as the number of stripper wells increased. The Camden Pool was discovered in 1934 and the Troy Pool in 1936. The Rodessa Pool, already important in Texas and Louisiana, was extended into the corner of Arkansas in 1937. The development of this famous pool in Arkansas was more rapid than it had been in either Texas or Louisiana, for the petroleum division of the Arkansas State Conservation Commission had dwindled to one field man and a stenographer. Also, the Arkansas conservation act of 1933 was entirely inadequate to cope with the Rodessa situation. Before the law could be changed, litigation had interfered with the officers to such an extent that the Arkansas part of the pool was dissipated by rapid drilling. Landowners, producers, and other interested persons petitioned for relief, and hearings were conducted. It was agreed that affected persons and firms would bear the expense of voluntary regulation and abide by the decisions of the conservation authority until the state could assume legal control. Early in 1939, at the request of Governor Carl E. Bailey, the legislature enacted a law creating a conservation board whose members served overlapping terms. Many persons looked upon this law as the most satisfactory one of its kind that existed, because it took advantage of the experiences of the other oil-producing states.

Arkansas' great Smackover Pool was a stripper area by 1937, at which time water encroachment had reached such a point that it was necessary to lift five hundred thousand barrels of fluid to gain twenty thousand barrels of petroleum. Nevertheless there was a demand for Smackover crude because of its asphaltic and lubricating elements. Many efforts were made to shut off the water by cementing, but that was difficult because all of the several producing horizons had been affected by the brine. Some of the wells produced one hundred barrels of water for each one of oil, and the situation was made worse by the fact that the brine was highly corrosive and contained a large amount of sand.

Exploratory drilling took place in twenty-seven counties of the state in 1937, when the Schuler Pool was discovered in Union County. Heavy-duty rigs capable of drilling ten thousand feet were required for the development of the Schuler area, which was expected to cover more than five thousand acres ultimately. The year after its discovery the Schuler Pool contained thirty-two producing wells, and more than twenty were being drilled. Each of these wells required more than two months to drill, at an expense of more than seventy-five thousand dollars.

The oil industry in Arkansas was seventeen years old in

1938, and there had been sixteen fields found on less than fifty thousand acres during that time. The industry had drilled 2,663 producing wells, the cumulative output of which had been nearly 450,000,000 barrels of petroleum. As the fourth decade drew to a close, one half of the revenue of the state came from the oil industry, although 90 per cent of the petroleum was from already depleted wells. Some of the strippers produced only nine barrels daily; at one time they had yielded thousands.

While dry wildcats were drilled in twenty-eight counties of Oklahoma in 1931, the chief interest of the industry there was the Oklahoma City Pool, where the low price of crude oil tended to reduce development. The Oklahoma City wells were quite expensive to drill, some of them using sixteen carloads of materials alone. In the first months of the year the price of crude oil dropped from eighty-nine to sixteen cents a barrel—largely the effect of the East Texas Pool. Governor William H. Murray proclaimed an emergency on August 5, 1931, and placed the militia in charge of twenty-nine Oklahoma oil pools, stripper wells excepted. He declared that the affected districts would remain closed until "the price hits one dollar." The state troops were removed from all excepting the Oklahoma City Pool in October. They were finally ordered away, but in 1933 the oil wells were administered by Colonel Cicero I. Murray, a kinsman and appointee of the governor's, with the Oklahoma Corporation Commission allocating production.

The first pump in the Oklahoma City Pool was placed in operation in 1934, a warning signal of the approaching decline of the output. Oklahoma City production continued to decrease so that in 1935 it was definitely in the artificial lift stage. There were more than eleven hundred wells on eleven thousand acres which had produced more than 250,-000,000 barrels of petroleum. In April an election was held in Oklahoma City to decide whether oil wells should be permitted in the eastern part of the city. The vote opened a large area to town lot drilling. A second ballot was taken in the spring of 1936, opening the State Capitol district on the north side of Oklahoma City to the oil industry. The day after the election, seventy-five wells were located and the digging of nineteen slush pits was started. By June, one hundred wells had been completed in the exclusive residential section of the city, and almost 150 drilling operations were in progress. The reservoir pressure was falling rapidly, so the new wells were allowed to flow open as long as they would, thus reducing the natural energy even more quickly. Virtually every city block in the proved area soon held at least one well, which amounted to a waste of millions of dollars by investment in unnecessary holes.

The restrictions in the northern part of Oklahoma City permitted a great deal of drilling; one block even had five wells. Governor E. W. Marland, formerly an independent oil operator, got for the state four hundred thousand dollars in consideration of a lease on the Capitol grounds, on which ten wells were drilled. It was said that these wells would be the most beautiful in the world. There would be no noise, except for the clicking of electrically driven machinery. Each well would be surrounded by a hedge of cedar, while vining roses blossomed on the derrick. Such beauty did not materialize, but the nights took on a gala Christmas appearance with thousands of strong electric bulbs glowing on the derricks. It was believed that the state might receive five hundred thousand dollars in royalties. Wealthy residents of the Lincoln Terrace section, near the state land, took to court the question of preventing oil development in that exclusive area, but they did not succeed in keeping the wells out entirely.

The competitive drilling of six-thousand-foot wells in the

Oklahoma City Pool became the subject of comparison with the development of the South Burbank Pool, a unit operation in Osage County started in 1934. The Oklahoma City wells in many cases cost one hundred thousand dollars, and they were spaced on an average of five acres of land apiece, despite the fact that the porosity permitted a hole to drain double that area. The wells of South Burbank cost about twenty thousand dollars each and were spaced for every sixteen acres. There was a rapid decline of natural energy at Oklahoma City, whereas at South Burbank the pressure had fallen little after two years. The wastes at the Oklahoma City Pool included useless drilling, too close spacing, loss of gas and pressure, excessive bonuses to lot owners, and the expense of pumping.

The installation of a compressor system for using the gas lift method in the Oklahoma City Pool cost about seventy-five thousand dollars. Other methods of pumping were expensive also. It was at this field that a centrifugal electric pump was developed, quite expensive itself but successful. It was predicted that many of the Oklahoma City wells never would become profitable, despite the desirable qualities of that particular petroleum.

The cumulative production of Oklahoma was approaching four billion barrels when the Fitts Pool was discovered in Pontotoc County in 1933. The wells of the pool had a low gas-oil ratio, and the pressure drop was unusually slow as a consequence. In five years the pool was extended to cover more than five thousand acres, and the total output was almost seventy-five million barrels of oil. Thirty-one fields were discovered in 1934 throughout the state, but the only significantly large one was the South Burbank, where the producing horizon was eighty feet thick. Seventeen companies owned leases in the South Burbank Pool, but the operations were placed in the control of one firm for the dual purpose of maintaining reservoir pressure and effecting economies. That plan of pool development became known as "unitization," and was looked upon as scientific. A deep well was drilled in the Fox Pool in 1935, indicating that in southern Oklahoma the sedimentary formations might be twenty thousand feet in thickness. The great Cushing Pool was twenty-five years old in 1937, and only a few more than two thousand of the wells were still producing an average of about five barrels of oil daily. The 3,600 wells in the pool had yielded a cumulative average output per acre of more than fourteen thousand barrels.

Between 1912 and 1939 the Osage Indians received a total of $114,160,000 from oil royalties and lease bonuses, a sum that was divided quarterly into 2,229 shares, or headrights. The Osages had fared better from the oil resources of their reservation than had the Five Civilized Tribes. The Osage tribe, after the allotment of the surface in severalty, continued to own their mineral resources in common, whereas the other tribes had divided the subsurface also. During the development of the oil industry, the members of the Five Tribes succeeded in keeping only a small part of their incomes from petroleum, while in many hundreds of cases they also lost their allotments. The total allotments of the Five Tribes amounted to more than 15,000,000 acres, but in 1940 only a little more than 1,500,000 acres remained in Indian hands.

From the exploratory viewpoint, one of the most interesting wells of the 1930's was drilled near Binger, Oklahoma, in 1934. The hole was one of the deepest in the state; at more than eleven thousand feet it produced a small quantity of petroleum. It yielded oil from a previously unexplored and unidentified formation, which caused geologists to believe that the pre-Pennsylvanian formations of western Oklahoma would be profitably explored in the future. Some

111

scientists were convinced that the expansion of the industry would take the form of deep wells in the sedimentary southern and western parts of the state.

Oil had been produced in Oklahoma chiefly in forty-one of the state's seventy-seven counties. The cumulative state production in 1938 amounted to 4,434,814,867 barrels from 55,627 wells. Between 1934 and 1940 the oil reserves of Oklahoma decreased annually except in 1936. In five years little more than half as much oil was discovered as was produced, indicating that Oklahoma's share in the future industry was declining. The output in 1940 was nevertheless more than three hundred million dollars in value.

In several respects the oil industry of the Southwest, whether Mid-Continent or Gulf Production, became a single unit during the fourth decade of the century. The Oil States Advisory Committee, a forerunner of the Interstate Oil Compact Commission, grew out of the military shutdown of the Texas and Oklahoma pools in the summer of 1931. The Interstate Oil Compact Commission was an attempt on the part of the states to exert a unified control over the industry that would avert Federal regulation. It was based on the various proration laws of the states, for which a testing foundation was laid by the National Industrial Recovery Act in 1934. After the Supreme Court of the United States nullified the National Industrial Recovery Act in 1935, the Connally Act prohibited the interstate shipment of illegally produced petroleum. President Franklin D. Roosevelt urged the oil industry not to fall back into its bankrupt condition of 1931, and the Oklahoma Legislature approved a plan for interstate co-operation. Representatives of the governors of the oil-producing states conferred at Dallas early in 1935, making specific plans for the Interstate Oil Compact Commission. Congress approved the compact six months later. Then representatives of the states attended a meeting at Oklahoma City in September, 1935; Governor Marland of Oklahoma was chosen chairman and a permanent executive secretary was selected. Whatever may have been the basic motive for the organization, those present agreed that its objective was the conservation of petroleum and not the raising of prices by limiting production.

Little was accomplished by the co-operative body until 1938, when the flush production of Illinois dislocated the markets of the established southwestern pools. The business of many southwestern oil firms became unprofitable, and at Oklahoma City it was suggested that all the oil wells of the United States be closed for fifteen days, thus removing a great quantity of petroleum from storage and creating a market for crude oil. The suggestion was not followed, but it indicated a co-operative attitude on the part of the industry itself.

By this time the Gulf Coast had definitely become the most important region for future development. There a zone 400 miles long and 125 miles wide contained more than 350 pools, the production from 50 of which indicated average yields of ten thousand barrels of petroleum an acre. Since the discovery of the Spindletop Pool in 1901, the Gulf Coast had produced 1,250,000,000 barrels, and at depths of more than eight thousand feet the region was expected to yield further immense quantities. A bright future was also predicted for the Permian Basin of West Texas and New Mexico, a region that in little more than ten years had produced almost a billion barrels of petroleum, a total which was in excess of the Louisiana output for thirty-five years or that of Pennsylvania for eighty years.

The number of wells that became pumpers increased rapidly as the fourth decade drew toward its end. A scientific estimate of the future national rank of the six south-

113

western states as oil producers placed Texas first. It was believed that the industry in Texas was 60 per cent developed, with a probable future production of more than seven billion barrels. New Mexico, thought to be about 16 per cent developed, was ranked third in the United States, with a probable future output in excess of two billion barrels. The Oklahoma industry was held to be three-fourths developed, with a future yield likely to be less than two billion barrels, which was fourth rank. Louisiana, Kansas, and Arkansas were looked on as about half developed, and none of them was expected to produce as much as a billion barrels in the future. These calculations were based on the proved reserves, porosity of the formations, and the possibilities of deeper drilling.

Petroleum had become one of the leading industries of the United States when the fourth decade closed, and the southwestern states contained about three-fourths of the known oil reserves of the country. One-fourth of the nation's wells and more than half of its reserves were in the state of Texas alone. The industry had become one in which billions of dollars were invested, with the control largely in the hands of the great major companies. The East Texas Pool had passed its flush period of production with illegal output virtually eliminated. The Interstate Oil Compact Commission, temporarily at least, had forestalled Federal control of the industry. The exciting Seminole and Oklahoma City pools likewise had passed their peaks and were declining; exploration and production in western Kansas and Texas were being carefully conducted by the major companies.

During these ten years the greatest volume of increase in petroleum production in the United States was made in the Texas and Louisiana Gulf Coast area. Within that region the greatest volume of increase was in Texas and the

PRIZE PHOTO BY CARL E. FEHRENBACH

A gasoline extraction and repressuring plant in Louisiana

Seismograph portable prospecting equipment

OIL & GAS JOURNAL

PETROLEUM ENGINEER

A portable hoisting unit used for cleaning out oil wells

largest percentage of gain was in Louisiana. There was an almost unbroken line of oil pools from the Rio Grande to the Mississippi, the result of several important factors. The elements contributing to this situation included the development and perfection of geophysics, the progress of deep drilling, the proximity of large refineries, and adequate carrying facilities. More coastal pools were drilled in this time than in all the previous history of the industry. The inaccessible coastal areas, it was believed, would be drilled in the future, at some time when fifteen thousand feet would not be an uncommon depth. By 1940 the state of Texas contained more than 23 per cent of the oil wells in the United States, and Oklahoma more than 14 per cent. This same year the six southwestern states produced 65.33 per cent of the petroleum of the country, Texas alone supplying 36.46 per cent. The percentages of the national output coming from the other five states were: Oklahoma, 11.50; Louisiana, 7.69; Kansas, 4.90; New Mexico, 2.89; Arkansas, 1.89. Texas' production was more than double that of California, its nearest competitor, and indications pointed towards the state's continued domination of the industry.

Scientific Advances

THE first years of the oil industry in the Southwest were far more speculative than scientific. The early drilling rigs were operated by either horsepower or manpower, using a weight-and-cable tool that was ancient in China. The original refineries simply boiled off the lighter parts of the crude petroleum in their effort to manufacture either kerosene or a lubricant of uncertain quality. Knowledge of the formation or possible structure of the subsurface of the earth as an aid in the finding of petroleum was sneered at. More oil men believed in "creekology" than in geology. "Find the oil and bail it out" was the theory on which the pioneers conducted their operations. If a new well would flow of its own energy, as was often the case after Spindletop in 1901, then the owner "let her go full force." In the production division, there was no thought of the future.

Four men were required to operate the best drilling tools of the 1880's. A common depth for the cable-tool holes of that time was six hundred feet; one thousand feet was unusual. Sixty to one hundred feet could be drilled each day by the alternate lifting and dropping of the stem and bit, which might weigh three thousand pounds. The cuttings were removed from the hole periodically by bailing. This sort of equipment cost about fifteen hundred dollars, and rarely did the completed well amount to more than twice that amount. By 1892 it had become possible to drill a well

116

two thousand feet deep, but with an outfit priced at ten thousand dollars.[1] Steel derricks that could be dismantled and moved, a great improvement over the less durable wooden ones, were introduced that year, but were seldom used. Wire lines replaced hempen rope as the years passed.

Especially outstanding in the advance of tools and techniques was the introduction at Spindletop, in 1901, of a rotary drilling bit. Earlier drilling of this type had been done in the Southwest, but attention was focused on it at Spindletop because of the caving that often prevented progress in drilling by the cable-tool method. The fishtail rotary bit cut the unconsolidated formations rapidly and tended to prevent the soft walls of the holes from caving. A second important discovery at Spindletop was the fact that muddy water not only helped to prevent caving but assisted in the removal by flotation of the cuttings or carvings. The use of nitroglycerin to blast cracks in the oil-bearing horizon came a few years later. Although cement was used in 1906 to stiffen soft walls and prevent caving, six years passed before it was commonly employed.

By the middle of the second decade of the century, when the deepest well in Oklahoma—then the leading state in petroleum production—was less than four thousand feet, drilling equipment had become heavy and rather elaborate. The weight of the drill pipe alone varied from ten to many more tons, depending on the depth; this was sometimes sufficient to result in deflecting the bit, which in turn made a crooked hole. Core barrels that would remove the core

---

[1] The tool of the standard, or cable, rig required the constant attention of the driller, for the bit had to be turned in the hole by hand. This tool might be deflected by a tough stone and drill a crooked hole, or the movement of the bit might cause soft formations to slip or cave. The rotary rigs that came later were of two types, one a fishtail wedge and the other a mechanism of revolving cones on which were especially durable teeth.

of the hole for scrutiny and geological study were being used. The teeth of some core bits were made of hard, black diamonds, which had the disadvantages of being quite expensive and subject to cracking or burning if they became hot. The combination of a need for greater strength as the wells went deeper and a steady advance in the price of rig timbers served to sell the more durable and movable steel derrick to the southwestern oil industry. Although in 1920 the average depth of the wells was less than three thousand feet, a great deal of prospecting was being done at nearly four thousand feet. By the close of the third decade, five-thousand-foot wells were common.

Several of the obvious disadvantages of drilling in the shallow waters of the Gulf Coast were overcome in 1932 by the construction of strong steel barges from which to work. The barges were 110 feet long and about half that wide. They were about ten feet deep and carried two diesel engines that generated electricity with which to drill. A derrick was mounted on top, and a supply of drilling mud was mixed in a great vat on board. When anchored for work, these barges would withstand rough water and hurricanes.

The difficulty and expense of marine drilling developed the desire to make several wells from one location. That wish was the parent of the whipstock, a device by which a slanting hole might be drilled intentionally. It became possible to drill seven wells at one location through the use of numerous whipstocks, which deflected the bit at suitable angles in exactly the desired direction. Another practical use of the whipstock was found in 1934 when a great wild well caught fire in the Conroe Pool near Houston, Texas. At a safe and cooler distance a crooked hole was drilled to tap and take the oil from the blazing well. Other fires brought about similar feats.

The movable rig had been common for years, but an

entire oil-field camp that was portable was introduced in 1934. In addition to the drilling equipment and machinery, the outfit included a kitchen–dining room unit with an electric refrigerator, and a bedroom-parlor with eight beds. Such luxurious comfort would have brought embarrassment if not tears to the tool-dressers of 1901.

Petroleum engineers had learned that too much pressure on the drill stem caused crooked holes, which were more difficult to make and troublesome to pump, and a remedy was found in the form of an electrical well-surveying apparatus. Periodic examination of a hole with this device disclosed deflections, thus the hole might be kept straight. Between 1937 and 1940 the engineers were quite busy with such technological problems and their solutions. Drilling had been made much easier through the construction of more than thirty types of equipment designed for different surfaces and subsurfaces. The "hard-rock" cone bit had permitted use of the rotary method in place of the churn-drill or cable-tool method in all sections of the oil country. Much less casing was required in rotary-tool holes, which reduced the cost of deep wells. These were also completed much faster, which likewise cut expenses. Repairs had been made easier through standardized machinery. The core head had been improved by the substitution of tungsten carbide, an inordinately hard alloy, for diamonds. An automatic weight feed was available to prevent excess pressure on the drill stem. A scientific efficiency study was made to discover the most desirable rotating speeds for bits in different formations. Elaborate investigations were made to discern the proper density for drilling mud.

A recent drilling novelty has been the "slim holes" of West Texas, the surface and inner casing of which were less than one-third the usual size. After eighty years of oil-well drilling, holes ten thousand feet deep have become common. Much greater depths are predicted, but countless scientific and technical difficulties will attend them.

The machinery and processes for making the holes were revolutionized, but the discovery of petroleum in the completed well always multiplied the technical problems that faced the oil man. A difficult and expensive problem existed if the well flowed with too great a pressure, and an equally troublesome question arose if it did not flow. Either the presence or absence of gas was attended with problems. Water of any sort was an obstacle. Most petroleum contained either paraffin, which might choke the valves and tubing or the pores of the oil-bearing stone, or asphalt, which tended to clog the producing horizon and reduce the flow of the crude oil.

In the early years of the century attention was often called to the great waste of gas, so in 1911 one company in the Glenn Pool constructed a plant to extract gasoline from natural gas. Each thousand cubic feet of the gas yielded about ten gallons of very high quality gasoline, which proved a most profitable undertaking. The production of many of the dwindling Glenn Pool wells was doubled by the installation of vacuum pumps.

The technicians of the United States Bureau of Mines argued that the reservoir energy in the oil pools was dissipated by permitting the gas to blow into the air. They demonstrated that the use of proper mud-laden fluid in drilling would prevent the gas from escaping, which would have the effect of retaining the pressure on the petroleum. That in turn would prolong the life of the oil field and increase the ultimate recovery of petroleum. The operators in 1913 objected to the use of mud-laden fluid because of the expense, however, and insisted that the lack of market made the gas valueless anyway. Pressures and volumes at times were so great that the escaping gas prevented deeper drilling to the oil, so the gas was permitted to blow itself out before the well was completed. In 1914 engineers of the Bureau of Mines readily shut off sixty million cubic feet of gas in a hole, and the well was completed without great delay. Still the producers avoided the use of mud because of the expense and their inability to sell the natural gas.

A new plan for producing oil in the Southwest was tried in 1925, when a shaft was sunk to the bottom of a shallow oil-bearing structure—about 130 feet. Horizontal holes were drilled into the oil-saturated sides, causing the petroleum to drain and accumulate in the bottom of the central hole. This enterprise, initiated by two men of Wichita Falls, proved the value of mining by producing about sixty barrels of petroleum daily. Mining was used to some extent to increase the recovery of the old shallow stripper area near Nacogdoches, Texas.

It was in the 1920's that a Russian engineer, Armais Arutunoff, induced a large oil company to finance the manufacture of a cylindrical, rotary, electric pump to lift fluids from the bottom of a well. He had devised this apparatus in his homeland for use in deep water wells. The pump, about forty feet long and four inches in diameter, was suspended in the wells by a cable and operated at a cost of about twelve dollars a day. A few alterations established the tool as a success in handling large amounts of water and oil together, and the operating cost was about one-fifth that of the air or gas lift.

One of the earliest efforts to increase the declining production of an oil well producing from a limestone reservoir was through the injection of hydrochloric acid. The acid was expected to dissolve the limestone at the bottom of the well so as to permit the crude oil to enter more rapidly. It injured the casing, however, and therefore was abandoned until inhibitors of corrosion were available to protect the steel. The use of acid to rejuvenate old wells proved a great success at Breckenridge, Texas, in 1932. This practice increased the production as much as 5,000 per cent in some wells where oil occurred in limestone or sand limestone mixture, and consequently became quite popular in later years. Technicians and scientists continued to multiply the methods by which more oil could be taken from the earth. A pneumatic pump which used the same air over and over again was introduced. An electrical gun that would shoot half-inch holes through casing and cement was perfected. This mechanism, making ten to fifteen holes like a machine gun before withdrawal, was especially valuable for opening wells to producing horizons that had been penetrated and shut off by the casing of the well.

The problems of the years that followed 1935 were varied and increasingly technical in their solution. The part played by the volume and pressure of gas in maintaining reservoir energy was studied carefully, with attention called especially to the Yates Pool in West Texas. After eight years of operation, the wells here produced at 80 per cent of their initial capacity, which was believed to be the result of careful handling of the reservoir energy. The wells of this and other fields have been prorated in production and the gas energy preserved by pinching in the flow under back pressure.

Another suggestion for increasing the yield of declining wells was made in 1912–13. It was proposed that water be forced into the oil-bearing formations to restore the pressure as well as to increase the recovery by flushing the petroleum from the sand. The process of water-flooding to increase production as used at Bradford, Pennsylvania, was inaugurated in Rogers County, Oklahoma, in 1931. Plans were made to recover the dormant petroleum of northeast-

ern Oklahoma and southeastern Kansas, where it was estimated that three billion barrels or more of oil could be produced by rejuvenation. The practice of water-flooding was
taken up also by the operators in Wichita County, Texas.
Both of these oil districts, old shallow producing areas, were
faced with a dire insufficiency of clear water, hundreds of
millions of barrels of which would be required for large-
scale flooding. Lack of water and the application cost of
about one thousand dollars an acre hindered the flooding
projects in several regions. Either air or natural gas com-
pressors also came into use for restoring energy in oil sands,
pumping these gases into certain intake wells in the field.
In fact, this process preceded water-flooding.

Throughout the southwestern states the producers of
petroleum wondered what to do with salt water. In some
areas the amount of water was small, but either it was increasing or there was fear that it would. In Kansas and
Oklahoma 1,000,000 barrels of water were produced with
every 650,000 barrels of oil. It was expensive to lift with
the oil, and it caused the casing to corrode. A photoelectric
apparatus was devised to locate the zone of brine intrusion,
so that the water could be stopped from coming into the
well. There were four methods, all expensive, of handling
brine. It could be plugged in the earth, pumped back into
the ground in intake wells, or stored in earthen tanks to
evaporate; or plants could be erected to remove the salt
from the water. In Kansas alone, four million dollars was
spent in 1938 on brine disposal. Operators in Texas and
Louisiana spent ten million dollars that year for the same
purpose.

Compared to the later plants, the early refineries were
extremely simple and grossly wasteful. The crude petroleum was treated in plain stills that removed the most vola-
tile parts—chiefly gasoline and kerosene. Gasoline was of

little value until the internal-combustion engine provided a quantity use and market. In 1913, when there were more than 1,250,000 motor vehicles in the United States, W. M. Burton, of the Standard Oil Company of Indiana, patented the cracking process of refining. Burton's system brought about a great change in refining by increasing the gasoline that could be made from crude petroleum. The stills were more complex and the processing done under considerable pressure. By 1922 the Indiana company had installed 295 pressure stills, and eighteen refining companies had been licensed to use the Burton method. At that time several other companies owned similar extracting processes. Although the older "skimming" plants were not eliminated, refining by cracking became far more important.

About two decades after the Burton patent was issued, the method of hydrogenation was introduced. In 1934 plants using the hydrogenation process were erected at Bayway, New Jersey; Baton Rouge, Louisiana; and Baytown, Texas. This scheme of refining was more involved and expensive than cracking, but it was more profitable. Hydrogenation tended to eliminate the refining residue of other systems by converting all the parts of the crude oil into gasoline. It highly improved low-gravity lubricating oils and permitted the practical elimination of gums and sulphur. It enabled refiners to make a staple low-knock gasoline.

Refining became more essentially a chemical process in 1935 when polymerization was introduced. Polymerization converted butane and propane from natural gas into gasoline of a much improved quality. Previously, butane and propane gases had generally gone unused.

By 1940 refining had experienced four different demands for the products of crude petroleum. Oil first was used to grease the axles of horse-drawn vehicles. Then coal oil (kerosene) was needed for lighting. Next, the internal-combustion engine required both gasoline for fuel and better lubricants from petroleum. Finally, aviation came with its demand for much better grades of gasoline and lubricants.

The crude oils of the southwestern states vary widely in their characteristics. All of them, light, heavy, good, and poor, must be processed for absorption by the world's markets. Although sulphur no longer is the obstacle that it once was to the refiner, either it or an excess of paraffin may reduce the desirability of an otherwise high-quality crude oil. The most desirable crude contains a large amount of high-quality gasoline and a liberal proportion of lubricants. One of the best crude oils is found at the Oklahoma City Pool, while from the East Texas petroleum good gasoline but poor lubricants are made. The oils of West Texas contain a great deal of sulphur, as do the products of some of the New Mexico and Kansas wells. Lubricants made from the Gulf Coast petroleum have low viscosity, which prevents American consumption, although they sell well to the European and Asiatic motorist.

As improvements in refining far more than doubled the life of the nation's oil supply, the search for petroleum passed from the necromancy of water witches to the laboratories of scientists. Seepages of oil and gas formed one of the most inviting attractions for the drillers of the early oil wells. There were cases of locating sites for oil wells with doodlebugs, incantations, and supposedly enchanted twigs, but surface indications throughout the Southwest were far more important. Geology was known and state surveys existed in the region for years before the petroleum industry was convinced that the science was of practical value. The Oklahoma Geological Survey, one of the youngest, was established in 1908 by Charles N. Gould. Reports published by this survey played a part in the discovery, extension, and limitation of the great Cushing Pool in 1912. The Newkirk Pool in Oklahoma was discovered in 1913 as a direct result of a geological map. From that time on geology was an asset to the oil industry, and several other pools were traceable to it. The discovery of the Eldorado and Augusta pools in Kansas in 1916, wholly through geology, further awakened oil company executives to the value of the science in finding petroleum. Surface geology, by which favorable structures were discovered, reached the height of its importance between 1919 and 1925.

Subsurface mapping, supplemented by the core drill, was started in 1919, and was followed the next year by aerial photography, which accurately portrayed the topography. Aerial photographic maps were especially desirable for companies that were planning pipe lines. The use of micro-paleontology was the natural development of the use of subsurface mapping, for the microscopic examination of the samples assisted greatly in the correlation of horizons, especially in wells drilled with the rotary rig, the drillers' logs of which were practically unintelligible for geological data.

One of the most successful methods of finding oil-bearing structures was introduced on the Gulf Coast about 1924: the use of geophysical instruments. Through a study of the reactions to these instruments it was possible to discover the coastal salt domes, even when there were no surface indications. Although some of the domes have not held petroleum, it has been known since the time of the Spindletop Pool that the salt intrusions caused the formation of traps for oil and gas. More than one hundred salt-dome pools were revealed as a result of the geophysical search. The four chief instruments were the original torsion balance, the magnetometer, the seismograph, and the more recent gravity meter. The large oil companies organized departments in this field and maintained their own geophysical crews.

While the use of geophysics spread from the Gulf Coast to most parts of the six southwestern oil states, other scientific assistance was developed to search for petroleum. A better core barrel was devised to permit the removal of the entire core from a well. For the sake of improving the accuracy of subsurface mapping, an electrical logging apparatus was made. Geochemistry was introduced, but was not accepted at once by the industry. This chemical prospecting was done by a laboratory analysis of a sample taken from the earth at or slightly below the surface. It was believed by some that the presence of ethane, butane, and propane gases in this soil proved the existence of petroleum at much greater depths. Texas and Oklahoma in 1934 required that complete logs of all wells be filed as official records for the information of the industry.

A new method for the surveying and logging of wells in which the casing had already been set was discovered in 1939. The levels of the different sands and strata were determined by measuring the intensity of the gamma rays that radiated through the pipe from the different layers of rock.[2] These rays were recorded electrically on a chart. This method had the advantage of being usable after the casing had been installed, instead of requiring an open hole. The fluoroscope was being used too, to detect the presence of oil in the returning mud-laden drilling water while the hole was being made.

As 1940 approached, most of the surface of the southwestern states had been mapped from the air, millions of dollars had been expended on geophysical surveys, and better coring and logging was becoming a general movement.

[2] Gamma rays are very short waves emitted by radium or other radioactive minerals.

The careful study of the formations through which a drill passed was fostered by thoroughly economic impulses. Such study was expected to determine the recoverable reserves of the future, at the same time obviating much useless re-drilling and exploring. Oil-bearing formations that had been concealed in the mud by rapid drilling would be discovered through laboratory analyses of the cores and cuttings. The operator would know the exact depth at which to perforate a casing so that he might tap several producing horizons with one well.

By the end of the fourth decade of the century the south-western oil industry had become completely technical. Powerful engines and strong rigs could drive bits nearly three miles into the earth, at locations selected by painstaking study of the subsurface. The drilling itself was done with a great deal of research and precision. When the well was completed, the production of the petroleum no longer was carried on with careless abandon, but rather with the intention of recovering the maximum amount of oil with the minimum of waste and cost. The processing of crude oil had changed from simple distilling to gain kerosene to a chemistry that produced hundreds of commodities. The search for unknown deposits of petroleum had gone far since the dark man in a frock coat carried a mysterious black box known as a doodlebug and muttered strange words. The scientific geologist and petroleum engineer had proved not only practical but invaluable. Other scientists, the physicists and the chemists, had brought their training and knowledge to the search for and production of petro-leum and natural gas.

◇◇◇◇◇◇◇◇◇◇◇◇◇◇◇◇◇◇◇ VI ◇◇◇◇◇◇◇◇◇◇◇◇◇◇◇◇◇◇◇

Peddling the Milky Way

P ROMOTERS began to sell stock in oil companies of the Southwest as soon as Captain Anthony Lucas discovered the first coastal salt dome at Spindletop. Some of the shares were in legitimate business enterprises, although all investment in the oil industry at that time was thoroughly risky. Stock exchanges were organized at Beaumont, Galveston, and Houston, and in two years 2,267,570 shares were sold at the Houston market alone. More than four hundred oil companies were organized; at least eighty of them were capitalized, and stock was issued for more than one million dollars in each.

The total capitalization of the Spindletop companies exceeded two hundred million dollars. Some of the firms were not really interested in entering the oil business honestly, but in order to sell stock they needed some sort of leaseholdings. Generally the leases of such firms were of no known value, and it was thus that Spindletop became "Swindletop." A few of the Spindletop companies prospered, certainly, and one of them paid dividends of 265 per cent in nine months. The sale of most of the stock, on the contrary, was considerably like peddling the Milky Way to a buyer who was a sucker caught on the bait of quick riches. He was told by the promoter, whether the par value was one cent or one dollar, that the shares represented the investment opportunity of the century.

The Spindletop stock-selling frenzy had not subsided when the well at Red Fork, in the Indian Territory, stimulated another outbreak. Thirteen companies, capitalized for a total of nine million dollars, were organized in the Oklahoma and Indian territories. Two of them produced oil. In the Indian Territory at that time it was possible for three men with twenty-five dollars each to charter a corporation and issue capital stock amounting to one million dollars. The law required only that three shares of stock be sold before the clerk of the Federal court at McAlester issued the charter. Oil companies were organized by the hundred in Muskogee and other Indian Territory towns. A Spindletop stock salesman offered the owners twenty thousand dollars for the little Red Fork well and a few acres that surrounded it. He admitted openly that his intention was to sell a vast amount of stock.

When the Wheeler well of the Santa Fé Railroad shot oil one hundred feet into the air in 1905, Ardmore, Indian Territory, became the center of a very active stock-selling boom. During the few years that followed, the allotted Indians of the Five Tribes were considered legitimate prey by many white men, as more and more petroleum was discovered. From 1906 onward, a systematic and corrupt fleecing of the Indians took place. This was done largely through the unmerciful and selfish actions of the men whom the county judges placed in charge of the Indian estates, as guardians. Some of the guardians were thoroughly honorable, but they were a minority. All of the dishonesty was not the work of white men, either, for there were many part-blood Indians with the cleverness of the Anglo-Americans and a native understanding of the tribesmen, whose confidence they possessed. Most of the allottees were willing to lease a piece of land all day to one oil man after another, a situation that gave validity to the first instru-

*From spring pole and knee action to steel and elbow grease, the differ-
ence is only technical; drilling still means labor*

*Marine drilling, with rig set on piling; and barge drilling
on the Louisiana Coast*

ment that was recorded officially. The result was a rapid change in the landownership throughout the eastern part of Oklahoma, which had been the Indian Territory. It was estimated that 90 per cent of the unrestricted Indians had parted with their land by 1916, and that in the future the tribesmen would be reduced to a race of poor tenant farmers.

A national advertising campaign to sell stock was conducted by one promotional company at the time the Cushing and Healdton Pools were attracting the most attention. That company was authorized to issue sixty-one million dollars worth of stock, which was more than the capital of the Standard Oil Company of Indiana. It represented a type of investor-fleecing that was to reach its peak about the close of the First World War, when, because of government bond sales, thousands of persons had become accustomed to owning securities. Doubtless many of the promoters had no definite intention or actual desire to take money dishonestly from their investors, but many others were entirely without compunction or scruples.

In a broad classification, there were four types of promoters. There was the honest but inexperienced and nonprofessional man who might make a profit for his company through a fortunate accident. There was the dishonest but nonprofessional promoter whose chief activity was that of avoiding the sheriff, and who had no intention of sending his investors a dividend. The third type, the dishonest but experienced and professional oil man, might make a profitable enterprise of his company and pay dividends if he were carefully watched. Finally, there was the honest and professional oil man who promoted companies, was well acquainted with the industry and its vagaries, and seriously attempted to make money for his shareholders.

Hazards were present in the oil industry that did not

exist for the investors in many other industries. Petroleum was expensive to obtain and its location uncertain; in addition, it was subject to fluctuations in price and was quite costly to prepare for the consumer. At the time of the greatest stock-selling activity the production of petroleum was haphazard, and the output of wells declined so rapidly as to interfere with the payment of dividends.

The fact that so many of these fraudulent promotional schemes emanated from Texas gave the stock of all Texas companies a decidedly unsavory reputation. There were four steps in a rather typical plan of promotion in Texas which was not an especially frenzied scheme. First a notice was published in the papers announcing the organization of the company, with the names of the officers and directors. A highly respected and well-known citizen, generally a banker, would appear as president. This individual would sell the use of his name during the stock-selling period and then publicly resign at a reorganization meeting. The newspapers next would print a story telling the readers that the generous directors were willing to share the profits that were certain to accrue. A limited amount of stock in this good company would be offered to the investing public. The third step was a large advertisement of the company's stock, followed in a few days by announcement that the demand for the shares was forcing the price to rise. The final step in this pattern was the announcement, if it was true, that the company had struck oil. Newspapers, knowing the ephemeral life of such enterprises, sold this advertising only for cash.

Some of the promoters added inducements to their stocks in various forms. One of these plans was to "guarantee" the investments. A West Texas company with a large lease, probably worth one thousand dollars, was capitalized at one million dollars. Stock amounting to five hundred thousand dollars was sold to the public with a promise that the money would be invested in government bonds which then would be used as security in borrowing operating capital. In addition, a bank agreed to repay the investors' money at the end of five years if a dividend were not available by that time. On a comparative basis, this was a safe oil investment for that day.

A swindling scheme that had nothing to do with stock-selling was developed at Ranger during the great oil boom there. It consisted of obtaining an option to lease a plot of land a few days before a near-by well was completed. On some pretext, the payment for the option would be delayed until the well was completed. If the well was a good producer, the holder of the option would sell it at a fancy price and pay the owner of the land his small fee. If the well was dry, the holder of the option would tear up the contract and refuse to pay.

Another scheme, definitely a swindle, that developed during the Ranger-Burkburnett hysteria consisted of selling "oil lots." The lots were plots of land large enough to hold the foundation of an oil derrick, but not large enough to cover sufficient reservoir space for a commercial well. They were sold by the thousands from New York to Hawaii, to persons who were led to think that large revenues would result. The popularity of the "oil lots" proved the gullibility of investors who were ignorant of the oil industry.

Every known plan of promotional finance was used, and some new schemes were devised, in the hectic boom years of 1918–23 in Texas. A few photographs of oil wells and credit with a printer constituted all the assets needed by some of the rapidly talking gentlemen. Some made money and paid their investors, others disappeared. Some leased half an acre of land in an oil field and issued vast amounts of stock in their companies. The leases of some of the promoters were fifty to one hundred miles from the nearest oil pool.

Investors from New York to Seattle, from San Diego to Miami, were estimated to have put billions of dollars into oil stock. In New York, officials of the state considered filing criminal charges against stock salesmen. The Governor of Texas and the Federal Reserve System issued warnings against buying oil stock. Texas officials decided to demand proof of the assets of all companies that were capitalized at one hundred thousand dollars or more, but the promoters evaded that curb by organizing several smaller companies on the same proposition. The stock was issued in units ranging from ten cents to one hundred dollars, although the most common shares were either one or ten dollars. Everyone from the shoeshine boy to the mayor might become the owner of oil stock, and thousands of elaborately embossed certificates were distributed throughout the United States. The stock certificates pictured derricks, refineries, strings of tank cars, and stacks or bags of gold.

At Burkburnett, where during the boom a city lot sometimes had an oil well in both the front and back yards, it was not unusual for an oil company to be organized and all the stock sold before the promoter had paid a single dollar. First he would get a contract of sale for a lease on a drilling location, very likely a front yard. The contract would be placed in escrow. Then, on the stationery of the Bigger Dividend Oil Company, on which the printer's ink was scarcely dry, he would write the names of the officers of the company, the location of the well, the capitalization of the company, and the par value of the stock. A sentence similar to the following would be written: "I, the undersigned, hereby subscribe to stock subject to the provisions of the Declarations of Trust to be made of record." Lastly, the stationery would be ruled with lines for names, addresses, and number of shares bought. The promoter was ready for business; with these sheets in his hand he would search for buyers. The latter would sign their names on the lines and pay for the stock. When all the stock had been sold, maybe fifty thousand dollars worth, the promoter would deposit fifteen thousand dollars at the bank for drilling the well and put the remainder of the money into his own pocket. He had made thirty-five thousand dollars in less than a week, and the stockholders of the Bigger Dividend Oil Company would get a fifteen-thousand-dollar hole in the earth that might produce oil.

Promoters of oil companies were no more busy and efficient than those whose activities included railroads, towns, and politics. When the Ranger boom excited the Southwest after the First World War, railways were projected to serve the region. With the construction of the railroads, townsites were laid out for oil boom towns. The town lots were sold at auctions, at which the purchasers paid 30 per cent cash and the remainder in installments. Thousands of persons attended the auctions, out of which sprang the towns of Jakehamon, Edhobby, Brekwalker, Jimkern, and Frankell. Those names were devised by linking together as one word the first and last names of men. They were typical oil boom towns that soon passed out of existence. By 1925 the last remaining store of Jakehamon, once a busy village, was closed, and a reinforced concrete block that held a safe became a gravestone of a dead community.

During this period the promoters of oil companies were converting the city of Fort Worth into a mecca for the "get-rich-quick" manipulators. The lobby of the leading hotel became a stock exchange, where men with leases on a few acres of mesquite trees boasted that they had never drilled a dry hole. In truth, many had never drilled a well at all. The sale of stock through personal canvass was too slow, so direct mail campaigns were used. The promoters were assisted, unintentionally, when the opinions of an "expert" were published in important financial and industrial periodicals. The "expert" predicted that the Ranger area would produce oil with a value in excess of ninety-five billion dollars, which would "make the Count of Monte Cristo look like a piker." The price of the oil rose from $2.00 to $3.50, and much of the Ranger output brought a premium of 65c a barrel in addition. The prediction was that the pools occupied an area about 110 miles square, the development of which would keep a million men busy for a decade and require an investment of nine billion dollars. The draining of this great reservoir would require 174,000 wells using 100,000 miles of casing. The picture dazzled thousands who converted their war savings bonds into oil stocks.

Henry Zweifel, a former oil-field boilermaker, became United States District Attorney at Fort Worth in 1921. In addition to knowing the legal field, Zweifel was conversant with the oil industry, and it was he who put some of the fraudulent oil companies out of business. During his investigation Zweifel stopped the mails en route to promoters, and in one week salvaged $77,000 that had been sent by unsuspecting investors to a single company. In three weeks, Zweifel accumulated $359,000 from the mails of another promoter. In November, 1923, more than one hundred oil company promoters were facing charges in the United States district court.

The revelations of the trials were astonishing. In the offices of one company was found a "sucker list" containing the names of two million individuals, each of whom had purchased stock at least once. Some of them had been induced to "invest" several times. One promoter had paid six hundred dollars for a lease on 125 acres of land which had been the basis for selling ten million dollars worth of fraudulent stock. Another case featured a janitor at Fort Worth who was allegedly related to General Robert E. Lee. An oil promoter hired this man for fifty dollars a month to give his name to a company which was designed to appeal to investors of the Old South. The letters of the company were signed "General Robert A. Lee." Lee was sentenced to two years in prison, and the men who had promoted the company were each sentenced to ten. Again, a certain promoter "guaranteed" his investors gusher oil wells and a 700 per cent cash dividend.

The two promoters whose personalities attracted the most attention were Dr. Frederick A. Cook, the pseudo-discoverer of the North Pole, and S. E. J. Cox, his lieutenant, who spent part of his time at a headquarters at Houston, Texas. Cox promoted a fake company at Houston, which brought him a five-year prison sentence. He pleaded not to be sent to Atlanta, as one of the officers there had purchased some of his stock. Later, at Fort Worth, he was sentenced to an additional eight years and sent to Leavenworth Prison. Cook failed as an oil man despite the fact that he sold $1,500,000 of stock in a single company. Then he sold his valuable "sucker list" for six thousand dollars to a lesser promoter, who merged 110 decrepit and fake companies and sold thirty-five million dollars worth of stock. A man with the ability and talents of Cook could hardly be expected to quit such an exciting business. He merged 413 companies of dubious assets and employed eighty-five stenographers to assist him, constantly invoking the assistance of the Almighty. Even the latter did not save him from a prison sentence of fourteen years and a fine of twelve thousand dollars.

137

Royalty shares have been the basis for one of the most recent developments in oil speculation. Possibly more than in any other sort of speculative selling, the promoter here relies on the complete ignorance of the purchaser. Many persons, living far from the oil country, have the impression that the ownership of a share in an oil well is a synonym for riches. These persons became the easy prey of men who sold minute shares in the royalties of producing wells. The one-eighth royalty of a well in the Oklahoma City Pool was divided into millionths and sold. Some northern and eastern purchasers expected sizable incomes from their royalty holdings, only to learn that years would be required for the accumulation of five dollars from them.

In the history of the southwestern oil industry, thousands of companies have been promoted and a few have prospered. Of the hundreds that were formed during the Spindletop boom, three became permanently important— the Texas Company, the Gulf Oil Company, and the Humble Oil and Refining Company. Few of the men who promoted oil companies made lasting fortunes, and most of those who gained wealth did so by conservative business methods. The successful operators were willing to risk losing their own capital, which at times they did, while unscrupulous and fraudulent promoters did not remain to take an active part in the growth of the industry. Most of the imposters who promoted speculative companies were outsiders in the industry. They were men who would have sold anything that caught the public fancy, from railroads to diamond mines, and cannot be looked on as belonging exclusively to the oil industry. The unfortunate part of the speculation in oil companies was the fact that most of the investors were persons who could ill afford to lose.

138

The Natural Gas Industry

W HEN, in 1879, a farmer at Greenvine, Texas, ignited the gas in his water well while lighting his pipe, he became a pioneer in what was to be an important southwestern industry. That farmer piped the gas into his house and became the first known domestic consumer in the region. Thus the southwestern natural gas industry may be said to have been started modestly by a pipe-smoking farmer who was quick to see the efficiency and convenience of a fuel that required no chopping or carrying and which left no smoke. The first steps in the development of the natural gas industry were faltering, beset with difficulty and hesitation. The time was to come, however, when many cities far removed from the source of supply would depend on the wells of the southwestern states for fuel.

Although Texas may be credited with the beginning of the industry, that state was left behind by Kansas, where gas, discovered at Paola in 1873, was displacing coal by 1886. In Arkansas, a well not far from Fort Smith introduced natural gas in 1888, but the discovery was not commercialized. By 1889 more than two hundred thousand dollars had been invested in the gas industry in Kansas, Texas, and Arkansas, and the annual sale of the product was in excess of fifteen thousand dollars. In Kansas, the towns of Paola, Iola, Osawatomie, Cherryvale, and Coffey-

139

ville soon were being supplied with it. The introduction of gas to the city of Neodesha played a part in the Fourth-of-July celebration in 1894. At Independence, a pipe was erected against the municipal flagpole so that a flare blazed at the top. A wild well near Sedan attracted national interest, and several excursion trains brought sightseers from the East to view it. In spite of these exciting events in Kansas, it was not until 1901 that Corsicana became the first Texas city to be supplied with gas. By that time the Kansas product was valued at more than three hundred thousand dollars.

To serve Kansas consumers, a pipe line 150 miles long was laid in 1902 from wells near Independence, initiating the method by which natural gas was later to be transported in increasing quantities. While the gas industry was thus furthest advanced in Kansas, it also began to develop in the Oklahoma and Indian territories, where the production was valued at $360 in 1902. It was generally sold at a flat monthly or annual rate, which permitted the consumer to burn as much as he pleased—until about 1905, when meters were devised to measure the amount used. The cost of gas was about one-half that of coal, and it obviated the need for firemen in such small plants as brickkilns. Forty-two small firms in what was to be Oklahoma were in the gas business in 1905; Tulsa, Bartlesville, Newkirk, Pawhuska, and Blackwell were being supplied with the fuel.

While the economies of gas attracted consumers and assured an increasing market, important events occurred in the industry in both Louisiana and the future state of Oklahoma in 1906. A farmer had discovered gas near Oil City, Louisiana, in his water well in 1904, but two years elapsed before holes were drilled in Caddo Parish and pipe lines laid to supply the residents of Shreveport, Mooringsport, Blanchard, and Caddo City. Thus Louisiana became the fifth southwestern state to develop this industry. In Oklahoma, a legal and economic argument began in 1907, as a constitutional convention considered the basic laws for the embryonic state. By the year of statehood, 1907, Oklahoma's gas industry was estimated at nearly five hundred thousand dollars. The presence of large quantities of gas in many big oil wells aroused two reactions. The oil producers in some cases considered that the gas was a nuisance and should be blown away as rapidly as possible. Sometimes it caught fire and the flames could be seen for many miles. Other oil men argued that though it was worthless at that time, the gas was valuable for factories, and that many industries should be attracted to Oklahoma by the abundant and cheap fuel.

With the intention of developing a large local market, the Tulsa Commercial Club petitioned the constitutional convention to prohibit the transportation of natural gas from Oklahoma. The economies, it was believed, would be so attractive that the industries would come to the fuel supply if they could not have it brought to them. The Tulsa group even asked other similar organizations to join in the campaign. T. N. Barnsdall stimulated the desire for factories in Oklahoma when he organized the Kansas Natural Gas Company. Barnsdall openly avowed that he intended to supply the city of St. Louis from Oklahoma wells, provided that he could gain control of at least 150,000 acres of gas-producing land. Early in 1907, while the constitutional convention was still in session, Guthrie, the territorial capital, became the mecca for men from all parts of the Oklahoma and Indian territories who were interested in gas. Mayors, city attorneys, commercial clubs, and oil men convened to discuss "Oklahoma gas for Oklahomans." They succeeded in causing the enactment of a law prohibiting the out-of-state sale of gas.

Flush Production

Litigation followed when Barnsdall defied Oklahoma laws in his plan to pipe natural gas to St. Louis. The first official act of Oklahoma's first governor, Charles N. Haskell, was to cause the arrest of a crew of laborers who were attempting to connect a gas line across the Kansas boundary. Although Oklahoma officials argued that the national government could not interfere with state laws, the litigation soon reached the Federal courts through an interpretation of the Fourteenth Amendment to the effect that a state could not prevent a citizen from selling his goods where he could find a market. The oil and gas men soon objected to the Oklahoma law on the ground that it was definitely retarding their business. That was a blow which the law could not withstand, so the act only marked the chief effort of Oklahoma to prevent interstate traffic in gas. In 1909 a Federal court sustained an injunction permitting gas to be piped from Oklahoma, while later the state law was declared to be unconstitutional.

Although it had been done three years earlier in Kansas and Oklahoma, not until 1909 was a large domestic distributing company organized in Texas; there the Lone Star Gas Company was formed to bring fuel from Petrolia to Fort Worth and Dallas. A pipe line 130 miles long was laid in 1910 to transport the product of this Clay County field to the two large northern Texas cities. That was the first long gas pipe line in the state, but in the next fifteen years many Texas towns were served by the same means.

While immense quantities of gas, associated with oil, were found at the Glenn and other smaller pools in Oklahoma, one great gas pool was discovered in 1907. It was the Hogshooter Pool in northeastern Oklahoma, from which vast quantities of gas were taken. Since the market was limited, little care was given the wells at that time, and the huge pool, a dozen miles long and, at its southern end, four miles wide, was squandered from 1909 to 1912. It was the chief source of gas consumed in Missouri and parts of Kansas. An eighteen-inch pipe line was laid from the pool, which in 1911 yielded gas at the rate of 1,264,000,000 cubic feet daily. So rapidly was the output taken from the pool that the pressure fell at the rate of one pound a day in 1912, causing water to enter and ruin many of the wells prematurely.

The excessive supply of gas sometimes caused odd incidents. Near Tulsa the owner of a large gas well wanted a night picture made of his property, so a photographer was taken to the scene, and the well was ignited with a sky-rocket. The photographer got the picture, but the owner received an expensive lesson in the difficulty of extinguishing a burning gasser. A railroad commercialized another burning well several miles from Muskogee, arranging an excursion train to the well.

The hasty removal of the gas resulted in too rapidly exhausting the Hogshooter Pool, an example of one of the wastes that became prevalent in the Southwest. Another of the chief wastes was the tardy closing of the wells, one of which, in Caddo Parish, Louisiana, flowed for years because the owner would not have profited by capping it. When, as late as 1910, the citizens of Bartlesville, Oklahoma, heard thousands of cubic feet of gas blowing away, they made no complaint about the great waste of an irreplaceable natural resource; instead they declared that the noise made sleeping difficult. Freeing the gas to gain the oil also resulted in an important loss, for in some instances several million cubic feet were blown away to get ten or twenty barrels of petroleum. In some of the pools the gas under its natural pressure was used to drive steam engines; but when released from pipes at the bottoms of wells to raise the oil, it was permitted to escape from the flow tanks that were not vaportight. The practice of selling it at a flat rate to consumers caused much loss through careless burning.

After the municipality became a consumer of natural gas, officials of Kansas City were induced to investigate the possible supply for the future. They were informed that plenty was available to supply the city for two or three years, so an effort was made to reduce waste through careful handling. As a result of the investigation, the Secretary of the Department of the Interior was requested to permit larger lease blocks of Indian lands in Oklahoma so that the gas companies might be assured of supplies for the future. In 1912 the size of the gas leases on Indian land was doubled to permit a total of 9,600 acres to one individual.

The annual physical waste in the Mid-Continent region by 1913 was estimated at 425,000,000,000 cubic feet, which, at the prevailing rate of consumption, was enough to have supplied the state of Oklahoma for sixty years. At the Cushing Pool alone it was believed that the gas wasted in a year was equal in heating power to more than five million tons of coal. Since there was no market for much of the gas in Oklahoma and Kansas, it was burned in more than two thousand great torches, or flambeaux. The large waving flames on tall pipes cast wierd shadows across the paths of travelers at night. Near Tulsa a well producing about sixty-nine million cubic feet daily was permitted to flow until it was exhausted. Some persons believed that the gas that was wasted was worth more than the oil that was produced.

These great wastes caused the United States Bureau of Mines to send experts into the area in 1913 to demonstrate more economical production methods. In the Cushing Pool the government men demonstrated the use of mud-laden fluid in completing oil wells so that the gas was sealed off and remained in the earth. The process was expensive, however, and the oil producers were slow to use it.

With the intention of reducing the waste and improving the market, the Oklahoma Legislature in 1913 passed an act that limited the gas to be taken from each well to one-fourth of the well's open-flow capacity. The act also required that the product be taken from all parts of the pool proportionately. Finally, it provided that pipe-line companies could not own wells or leases. Another effort to prevent the waste of gas was made in 1915, but it aroused objections from oil men on the ground that closing the gas wells would injure the petroleum industry. The Oklahoma Corporation Commission was empowered to regulate the gas industry, so members of that body conducted hearings throughout the state to gather information. A legal effort to save the gas was also made in Texas, by prohibiting wells from flowing until a market was available, but the law did not apply to wells operated for oil.

In Louisiana one of the world's great gas pools was being developed near Monroe in 1917. The pool had been discovered in 1909, and as more wells were drilled, a fuel supply sufficient for all of Louisiana and much of Texas, Arkansas, and Mississippi was found. The Monroe Pool was estimated to contain more than four trillion cubic feet of gas, but even it was overshadowed in size by the development of the Panhandle Pool in Texas, which was discovered in 1918. By 1925 the Panhandle Pool had been extended to cover 1,350,000 acres, with an estimated ultimate production of sixteen trillion cubic feet; it was recognized as the world's largest gas pool. Large pipe lines were laid from both of these pools. The first "all-welded" gas pipe line was laid from the Monroe Pool to Beaumont and Port Arthur, to be followed later by transporting systems that took the output of the Texas Panhandle to Monterrey, Mexico.

Three of the longest gas pipe lines in the United States were constructed in 1931–32 from the Panhandle Pool. One of them, 1,200 miles long, extended to Illinois and Indianapolis; another 1,855 miles long, to Minnesota; and the third, 950 miles long to Chicago. Several shorter lines were also laid, to make a total of 4,500 miles of pipe, much of which was twenty-four inches in diameter.

The third immense gas pool, smaller than the Panhandle but larger than the Monroe, was discovered in western Kansas near Hugoton. In 1933 it had 115 wells, but there was little market for the output. These three enormous reservoirs made the Southwest far the most important gas-producing area in the world.

The wanton waste of gas in the Texas Panhandle in 1934 attracted the interest of both the industry and the Federal government. Perhaps 30 per cent of the Panhandle's product was wasted in the years of 1934–35, but it was reduced to 2 per cent by 1938, when production and consumption had been synchronized more effectively. The state law had previously permitted the freeing of the gas after the natural gasoline had been extracted, and the result was the wasting of enough of the treated commodity to supply the current market demand of the nation. The law was changed in 1935 to prohibit freeing the gas, whether classed as "sweet" or "sour." The latter was that which contained hydrogen sulphide in quantities that made it undesirable as domestic fuel. The law provided that "sweet" gas might be used only for fuel and light, whereas "sour" gas might be burned in the manufacture of carbon black.

By 1936 eight firms were believed to control 80 per cent of the gas consumed in interstate commerce, a condition amounting to monopoly. Remedial suggestions included Federal regulation of wholesale rates, security issues, and the sale of properties, as well as control of the

The torch and destructive effects of a blazing gas well

Fighting fire in a cratered gasser

Partially subdued but still stubborn

Lowering a "Christmas Tree" over the roaring well

The gas is still escaping but under control

volume in interstate commerce. The monopolistic condition was strengthened, however, when the United States
Supreme Court issued a decision in a gas case. The case
developed when the Texas Railroad Commission ordered
the owners of pipe lines to purchase the output of producers who did not own transporting facilities. The purchasing was ordered despite the possibility that the pipe-
line companies might already have sufficient gas to supply
their own needs; they resisted the order and litigation followed. The decision of the appellate court was that the
pipe-line owners need not purchase the gas of the small
producers.

Natural gasoline, by no means characteristic of the area,
was the first significant product to be taken from the southwestern gas. Some efforts were made to extract the gasoline
from the wet gas of the oil wells early in the century, but
important accomplishments did not come until 1911, the
first year for which statistics for the region are available.
By 1912 the extraction of natural gasoline had become the
feature of the industry, and the next year there were forty
plants in Oklahoma alone. As much as three gallons of
gasoline, or more, might be taken from a thousand cubic
feet of gas. Natural gasoline was valuable because of its
high volatility, a dangerous quality that was unfortunately
demonstrated in the autumn of 1915 when a tank car ex-
ploded at Ardmore, Oklahoma, killing about fifty and injuring five hundred persons. It was used at refineries in
blending poor fuels to a better standard. As the automotive
industry grew and increased the demand for fuel, natural
gasoline grew in desirability as a blending agent.

The largest natural gasoline plant in the world, capable
of extracting more than ten thousand gallons of gasoline
from two million cubic feet of gas a day, was in operation
at Kiefer in 1915. Oklahoma led the United States in the

production of natural gasoline in 1913 and for several years thereafter, turning out more than half of the national output in 1917. The state contained 234 gasoline plants that year, which contrasted significantly with 1911, when there were only 8 plants.

The Natural Gasoline Manufacturing Association was organized in 1919 to promote the industry by calling attention to the economic features of the product. The removal of natural gasoline, it was pointed out, did not impair the value of the gas from which it was taken. Natural gasoline, when mixed with naphtha, produced a good motor fuel. The product had the effect of bringing the oil producers and gas men closer together, for there was profit in combining their commodities.[1] The extraction plants in some parts of the Southwest succeeded in taking several gallons of natural gasoline from each thousand cubic feet of gas, a situation that was highly profitable when the price was ten cents a gallon, and especially so when the wholesale gas rate was three cents a thousand cubic feet. Natural gasoline, however, became less important as the years brought technical improvements in refining processes, such as cracking and vapor recovery systems.

Three other products of the gas wells were assuming significance by 1914: propane, butane, and helium. Propane and butane were fractions of the gas that might be sold in tanks; thus at a later time they became important as fuel in areas not served by pipe lines. The first helium found in the Southwest was identified in Kansas about 1907, but it was discovered later in the gas of the Osage Reservation.

Helium is a gaseous element that was discovered in 1868 by a French astronomer who, during an eclipse, found the

[1] It should be borne in mind that natural gasoline comes from the vapor of oil wells as well as from gas wells.

sun to be surrounded by an orange-colored spectrum. The substance of the band about the sun was unknown, so it was named helium, after the sun itself. It was later isolated by research and found to be noninflammable and lighter than any other gas except hydrogen. The use of airships, both dirigible and nondirigible, during the First World War, and their susceptibility to fire when filled with hydrogen, accentuated the need for a safer inflatant. One hundred thousand dollars was set aside from the funds of the war and navy departments in 1917 for the development of a helium supply for military balloons. Semiexperimental plants for the extraction of helium from gas were put into operation at Petrolia and Fort Worth in 1919.

By 1924 there were three dirigible airships in the world, two owned by the United States and one by Germany, although there was a supply of helium available for only one. Some years later it was found that the gas of the Texas Panhandle contained a larger percentage of the element than the Petrolia product, so the older plants, on which the government had spent nearly eight million dollars, were abandoned and another constructed at Amarillo. The new plant was capable of producing two million cubic feet of helium a month, at a cost of about $13.23 per thousand. The Federal laws controlling the helium supply were changed in 1927 to permit the sale of the element to citizens of the United States. Great lighter-than-air craft were proved to be impractical, however, causing the military demand for helium to decline. Helium has become an important asset, more recently, in the treatment of respirational diseases.

Another valuable product of gas, carbon black, increased in importance throughout the Southwest. Carbon black, the substance deposited on a metallic surface in contact with the flame when gas is burned in air deficient in oxygen, first was used in 1864 in the manufacture of ink, but it soon found its place in other goods, such as polishes, paints, and rubber. It became important in the making of automobile tires, a use that increased with the years. Statistics dealing with carbon black are not available before 1919, but at that time Louisiana, second only to West Virginia, had seven plants, and Oklahoma and Kansas each had one. The manufacture of carbon black was especially adapted to pools far removed from cities, for the process required the burning of great quantities of gas, which caused dense black clouds of smoke to rise from the plants. Still more important in this connection was the desire to restrict the consumption of gas to domestic use; one carbon black plant might consume gas equal to the domestic requirements of a city of 250,000.

Louisiana was leading the country in the production of carbon black by 1922; and in 1926, with the increasing gas output of the immense Monroe Pool, the state yielded 72 per cent of the supply of the United States. It soon lost this leadership to Texas, however. The first Texas plant, costing three hundred thousand dollars, was constructed in Stephens County in 1923, and by 1930 the factories in that state, chiefly in the Panhandle, were making more than 70 per cent of the nation's supply.

The inefficiency of the plants manufacturing carbon black attracted the interest of E. P. Schrock, director of the Bureau of Industrial Chemistry at the University of Texas. He announced, in 1937, a method that would produce more than seven pounds of carbon black from one thousand cubic feet of gas, a fivefold improvement over the process then in use.[2] Carbon black plants were consuming more than 291,000,000,000 cubic feet of gas in the

[2] The product of Schrock's method, however, is reported to be of a quality with limited uses.

Texas Panhandle in 1937, at which time the state yielded three-fourths of the national supply. By 1940, 87 per cent of the carbon black of the world was being manufactured in Texas.

The development of the southwestern gas industry by 1940 had been responsible for the erection and operation of industrial plants throughout the six states. Natural gas had proved to be an ideal fuel for certain types of plants requiring an even heat, such as glass factories, brickkilns, smelters, and cement plants, which were numerous in the region. Hundreds of cities of the United States were supplied with natural gas for fuel. It was taken to the millions of consumers through thousands of miles of pipe lines, thus in some respects overcoming the chief natural disadvantage of the commodity—transportation. By-products of the southwestern gas were both important and diversified, ranging from carbon black, a vital ingredient of automobile tires, to helium, explosives, and formaldehyde. By 1940, Texas was the chief producer of natural gas and contained more than half of the country's known reserves. Louisiana, with its great Monroe Pool, followed Kansas in third place, and Arkansas, Oklahoma, and New Mexico all had great productive capacities and known reserve supplies.

Arteries of the Continent

AMONG the troublesome problems constantly facing the oil industry has been the question of transportation. In the early days of the business in Pennsylvania, the oil was floated down the creeks and rivers in barrels. As the demand for petroleum increased and the production grew, the industry logically changed to the use of pipe lines. The earliest pipe line in the Southwest was that laid from the shallow wells near Nacogdoches, Texas, but the enterprise was not a commercial success. The first significant and successful pipe line in the region was a short one from the oil wells to the refinery at Corsicana in 1897. At about the same time, paralleling the Texas development, lines were built in the vicinity of Neodesha, Kansas.

The laying of pipe lines quite naturally accompanied the construction of refineries, for the transporting and processing divisions of the industry were closely interlocked. Beaumont and Port Arthur, Texas, were the sites of refineries and were the termini of pipe lines soon after the completion of the Lucas well at Spindletop, and the Sour Lake Pool resulted in the laying of another line to Beaumont. Thus, while the century was still young, three refining and crude-oil transportation centers had developed in the Southwest—at Neodesha, Beaumont, and Corsicana. The petroleum of Kansas and northeastern Oklahoma was transported by the Standard Oil Company's subsidiary, the Prairie Oil and Gas Company, to Neodesha to be refined. The oil of eastern central Texas was taken to Corsicana for processing, while the coastal pools supplied the refineries at Beaumont and Port Arthur.

By 1903 the pipe lines in Kansas extended from Chanute and Humboldt to Neodesha, and Prairie wanted to enter the Indian Territory to take petroleum from the wells near Bartlesville. A special act of Congress was necessary to authorize the Secretary of the Department of the Interior to permit a pipe line to cross Indian land. After that delay the company laid the line as far south as Tulsa. In 1904, then, it was possible for oil from the Red Fork Pool to be taken by pipe as far north as Chicago, via Neodesha and Kansas City. The leases of Indian lands were limited to 4,800 acres in 1904 to prevent any person or firm from controlling too much producing territory. The transporting companies had only insignificant holdings of Indian allotments.

Opposition to the Standard Oil Company was rife in Kansas in 1905 when it was proposed in the legislature that the state assume the regulation of the pipe lines. The leaders in the movement even went so far as to suggest that the state should erect and operate a refinery and make all the lines common carriers. Another suggestion was that the state should construct a pipe line 933 miles long to the Gulf of Mexico, in order to give the producers an outlet. The legislature even appropriated four hundred thousand dollars to be used in the construction of a refinery, and the transporting firms were made common carriers with their rates regulated by the state. From 1901 to 1904 the Prairie Company had raised the prices of crude petroleum so that production had become profitable. Then, during the conflict with the legislature, the pipe-line company refused to purchase any petroleum of less than 30 degrees gravity, a

153

ruling which had the effect of barring much Kansas oil. At once the cry of "spite" was heard, but at that time oil of 30 degrees gravity was considered good only as fuel and not for refining.

The development of the prolific Glenn Pool in 1906–7 resulted in the first great pipe-line-laying campaign. Immense quantities of oil were produced, so Prairie quickly extended its line and became a buyer. More petroleum was produced than the one concern could move, however, causing the owners of the wells to resent the low price they received. They considered laying a co-operative pipe line to Muskogee and using the water of the Arkansas and Mississippi rivers to move their oil to market by barge. They also discussed the construction of a refinery of their own.

The remarkable output of the Glenn Pool was responsible for the laying of three long pipe lines from the area to the Gulf Coast, although the first oil went to refineries in Texas by rail. The Texas Company doubled its capital stock in 1906 and announced that it would lay a pipe line to the Glenn Pool. The Gulf Oil Corporation, a property of the Mellons of Pittsburgh, planned another. Both of these outlets were completed in 1907, when the third, to serve as a source of supply for the Standard Oil Company refinery at Baton Rouge, was announced. The Standard line, under the name of the Oklahoma Pipe Line Company, was completed in 1910. The construction of pipe lines such as these was quite expensive, for in addition to the cost of the line itself, pumping stations were needed about every forty miles. The routes of the Texas and Gulf companies' lines were more than four hundred miles long, a distance that the petroleum traversed in fifteen days.

As Kansas had been, a few years before, Oklahoma was infected with opposition to the Standard Oil Company by 1909, and the legislature enacted a law making pipe lines common carriers. The act, a result of the Glenn Pool congestion, required ratable purchases from all producers in an oil-producing area. It also prohibited transporting companies from owning oil wells. This law was altered in 1915, because of the immense output of the Cushing and Healdton pools, to limit purchases according to "reasonable market demand." It was in 1909 that Governor Charles N. Haskell of Oklahoma avowed that he would call a special session of the legislature to build a state-owned pipe line to the Gulf of Mexico, so that the oil men might oppose the Standard Oil Company. The third state to take up the question of regulating the pipe lines was Texas, where in 1917 a common carrier law was enacted giving the Railroad Commission control of the industry. The fascinating idea of a state-owned and state-operated pipe line cropped up again in 1935 when attention was called to the great waste of the Texas Panhandle gas. It was suggested that the Texas Legislature authorize the state to build a line to St. Louis and Detroit. Most of the money, it was believed, could be borrowed from the Federal government through the Public Works Administration. The state would organize a company and carry on all the usual business.

Federal scrutiny of the Standard pipe lines had started in 1906, and those taking oil across state lines had been placed under the control of the Interstate Commerce Commission by the Hepburn Act. The Interstate Commerce Commission filed a report in 1907 calling attention to the profits of the pipe lines. The cost of moving a barrel of petroleum amounted to two cents per hundred miles, according to the report. Through the Prairie pipe line, Standard took thirty-five thousand barrels of oil from Kansas and the Indian Territory daily. It purchased the oil cheaply at the wells, and with the low cost of transportation was able to sell its refined products in the competitive markets of the East at an advantage. Until 1910 the Standard Oil Company did most of the retail business in the United States, but with the development of the industry in the Southwest strong competitors arose.

The efforts of the Interstate Commerce Commission to establish its control of the pipe lines brought a legal contest that continued for years with the Prairie Oil and Gas Company. The reply of the latter in 1912 was that it owned almost two thousand wells with a daily production of more than eleven thousand barrels, while it had contracts to sell approximately one hundred thousand barrels. The company argued that it would not enter the business of being a common carrier, because that would prevent it from controlling the quality of the oil it handled. It never had been a common carrier, moving only its own petroleum. In its brief the company protested that the enforcement of the orders of the Interstate Commerce Commission would violate both the Fifth and Fourteenth amendments to the Constitution of the United States. These arguments were overruled, however, when in 1914 the United States Supreme Court upheld the Hepburn Act of 1906 by its decision in the Ohio Oil Company case. That decision definitely placed the pipe lines under the control of the Interstate Commerce Commission when they were doing interstate business.

A Federal Pipe Line Commission, of which Cato Sells, United States Commissioner of Indian Affairs, and Lieutenant James O. Richardson, of the United States Navy, were members, conducted hearings in Kansas, Oklahoma, and Texas in 1914. The purpose of the commission was to study the advisability of laying a pipe line from Kansas to the Gulf Coast to assure the Navy of a supply of fuel in case of emergency. Oil men opposed this plan as smacking of socialism.

The shortage of laborers because of the First World War

was cited as the reason a ditching machine was used in 1918 to lay a pipe line. The machine permitted the completion of a pipe line 113 miles long in four months, and presaged the passing of a picturesque character from the oil fields. He called a shovel a "canal wrench," and when the great pipes were melted together he vowed that he could "weld anything from a broken heart to the break of day." Pipeline laborers were something of a fraternity, in which each man was known by a nickname and no questions were asked. It was said that three crews worked on every job: one was coming to work, one was working, one was moving on.

Four large pipe lines were laid to the Ranger Pool in 1919, but the decline of the production left an excess of transporting capacity. By the next year, several thousand miles of pipe lines moved oil from the pools in Texas, Oklahoma, Kansas, and Louisiana to refineries, some of the latter in Illinois and Indiana. In the three years 1927–29, 5,500 miles of pipe lines were laid at a total cost of more than $150,000,000. Included in that construction were 3,800 miles of trunk lines, some of which took petroleum from the large West Texas and New Mexico discoveries to refineries on the Gulf. By 1932 the East Texas Pool alone had eighteen trunk pipe lines with a daily capacity of eight hundred thousand barrels.

On the Gulf Coast of Texas, Houston took its place as a great oil-exporting terminal. During the first six months of 1923, more than five million barrels of petroleum left Houston by tank ship. There were seven refineries, and eight other companies owned export storage facilities. It was possible to load or unload ships at the rate of six thousand barrels an hour. Tankers annually moved 113,000,000 barrels of petroleum from Gulf ports by 1926. Much of that oil was taken to refineries on the Atlantic Coast for processing, after having arrived at the loading dock by pipe line.

By 1936 Corpus Christi too had become an important exporting city, being the terminus of several large pipe lines and the site of several refineries. The pipe lines made marketing of the southern Texas oil a simple matter, taking the petroleum to a coastal town from which it could be moved cheaply by water. In the Corpus Christi district there were 104 pipe lines for oil, 1 for gasoline, and 35 for gas.

The first pipe line for transporting gasoline was laid from Luling to San Antonio in 1930. The success of that venture caused the Phillips Petroleum Company to lay an eight-inch line from its refinery at Borger, in the Texas Panhandle, to Kansas City the same year. This line held 232,000 barrels, and eight days were required for the gasoline to reach Kansas City. The following year, five companies united in the construction of a gasoline pipe line from Oklahoma to Kansas City, Des Moines, and Chicago. That line, known as the Great Lakes Pipe Line, enabled its owners to transport their finished products to the large markets of the Middle West. The transporting cost was low enough to permit competition with refineries in Illinois and Indiana.

Pipe-line systems were elaborate by 1940; they had become highly specialized parts of the oil industry. Trunk, branch, and feeder lines formed the chief divisions, but in addition there were terminals, storage yards, switches, pumping stations, and telegraph and telephone circuits. Airplanes were used to map the routes of projected lines, and the pipe was tested electrically for flaws. The pipe-line system of the Southwest, like the circulatory system of an animal, carried vital liquids for the nation.

158

Social and Economic Influences

I N all the ramifications of human existence, the petroleum industry fastened its hold on the states of the Gulf-Southwest. It was felt in the construction and growth of new and established communities as well as in the reactions and mental attitudes of the citizens. Admittedly, the most obvious social effect was the population shift, which brought hundreds of mushroom towns into being; but more lastingly important were the economic and political effects of the thousands of oil pools that were developed.

The discovery of a deposit of petroleum changed the life of every person living in a community. The crew of the wildcat well usually found living accommodations with a neighboring farmer or in a near-by town; then, with the announcement that oil had been found, the entire countryside at once began to pass rapidly through a transition. First came more lease buyers with their contract forms, busily searching out the owners of the land yet untaken. That small vanguard was followed in a few days by the crews, with rigs that went into operation on locations near the discovery well. With the arrival of the drilling crews, food and shelter soon became scarce and brought fancy prices. Farm homes became rooming houses and cheap wooden hotels were either erected or hauled to the community on trucks. If there already was a town conveniently near, food and shelter would be found there at outrageous rates. During the Burkburnett hysteria, it was not uncommon for a room in a private house to rent for $50–$60 a week; or a man might spend the night on a cot in a tent-hotel for $1.25. There were, however, many instances of men who spent whole nights walking the streets, having failed to find beds in the boom communities. Meals likewise were exhorbitantly expensive, especially since the waiter who served a two-dollar steak expected his tip to equal the check.

Those were obvious aspects of boom conditions that existed during the period of active drilling or flush production in the uncontrolled pools before 1938. More than three-fourths of the early arrivals were men, many of them unmarried. Families came later, bringing with them the need for schools. Some of the laborers had been farmers, and had deserted their fields and crop mortgages for the high wages of the oil industry. Many of the workers for the larger producing organizations became transient roustabouts, or drillers who moved from one new pool to another, from Kansas to South Texas or from Louisiana to New Mexico. With the passing of years and the acquisition of children, these men were often transferred to the less exciting occupation of minding the pumps in the established pools. Similarly stable was the work of the men who operated the relay stations of the pipe lines. In 1940, thousands of families throughout the Gulf-Southwest were living in relative comfort at the pumping stations or on the leases to which they had "retired" from the more strenuous field operations.

The influence of the oil industry on education was tremendous. With the arrival of the women and children at the flush pool, a school was soon started—assuming, of course, that no convenient place of education already existed. It would generally be in the incommodious home of one of the mothers who had once been an elementary teacher, and would be supported by tuition. From that beginning, a school district would be organized and a building constructed. In some instances, such as at McCamey, Texas, the plans were made for the school while the town was still only a community of tents. The taxable property in the expanding pool placed ample funds at the disposal of the school officials, who sometimes paid for ornately elaborate property. A stairway of marble adorned the high school at Kiefer, Oklahoma, when the Glenn Pool was a great producer. Stone buildings throughout the region were equipped as well and as expensively as many of the best metropolitan schools of the country. In many cases the faculties of the oil-field schools were better trained than the teachers of the older communities, and they received salaries in keeping with the excessive local living costs. During the period of the Ranger excitement, the influx of families crowded the schools so that the children could be instructed only in half-day shifts. Education of the young certainly was not neglected in the oil fields.

Elementary and secondary schools were by no means the only ones to feel the influence of the petroleum industry, however. Colleges and universities were affected both directly and indirectly. Outstanding, of course, is the University of Texas, the owner of a great expanse of oil-producing land in West Texas. The revenue accruing from the Big Lake Pool not only has transformed the campus at Austin but has made the university one of the richest educational institutions in the United States. In several other cases, colleges and universities of the region have received large gifts from the estates of rich oil men. Even more important has been the change in curriculum which the oil industry has brought to the advanced educational institutions. In the larger ones, schools of geology and petroleum engineering, have been organized, while most of the colleges and many of the high schools offer instruction in geology.

Churches in the flush areas also came into being about the time that women became numerous. The organization of a congregation often was the spontaneous result of the accumulation of families at the scene of a discovery. At Kiefer such a group first held its services in the shed of a lumberyard. Elsewhere, school buildings or brush arbors became meeting places. There were occasions when the oil company executives or owners encouraged the Sunday services by closing all lease operations that day. Laws also played a part in encouraging worship: at Drumright, for instance, motion pictures were prohibited on Sundays, and later, in Arkansas, a statute prohibited all but the most imperative field work on the Sabbath. Throughout the Gulf-Southwest the churches have felt the financial impact of the oil industry in the form of beautiful windows and decorations, and some of the most impressive temples of the region have been erected and furnished entirely through the beneficence of wealthy oil men.

Contrasting with the spiritual and educational growth of the oil country was the presence of the often overemphasized criminal element. It is probable that there were more murders and disorderly events here than in the more settled communities, but the criminals were numerically a small part of the boom populations. Most of them fell into two groups: those who committed crimes because they were removed from the restraining influence of home ties, and those who were confirmed outlaws attracted to the oil towns by the unusual amount of money in circulation. Their conflict with society created great reputations not only for the criminals themselves but for the peace officers of such exciting flush pools as Healdton, Ranger, and Seminole. Sometimes the outlawry of a boom area surpassed the ability

A 24-inch pipe line
traversing rough terrain

NATIONAL TUBE COMPANY

PETROLEUM
ENGINEER

Pipe line construction
at a stream crossing

Bypass around a meter
for "hot" (illegally
diverted) oil

OKLAHOMA PUBLISHING COMPANY

Shifts change at a Baytown, Texas, refinery

The varied elements of a great refinery on the Gulf Coast

of the local officers to gain control and resulted in martial law, as at Mexia and Borger.

Another fundamental change in the ways of the Gulf-Southwest occurred in the banking business, which was violently affected by the financial transactions of the oil men. While the bank was the last business institution to be established in the boom town, those already operating in the small agricultural villages were faced with the necessity of making drastic alterations in their policies to prevent bankruptcy. Even so, hundreds of them did fail and quit business. The chief problem of the oil-town banker was not that of acquiring sufficient funds, but that of keeping solvent after the boom. Established small-town bankers, on the discovery of near-by oil pools, suddenly found themselves with millions of dollars on deposit and numerous clerks keeping their accounts. Previously there had been only a few thousands of dollars in their vaults and two or three bookkeepers. The bankers were asked to loan money on such collateral as potentially productive leases, drilling rigs, refineries, or flowing oil wells. They were completely ignorant of the value of such property, because in the past their knowledge had been concentrated on commercial loans and agricultural mortgages. The quick demands of the oil business required fluid investments instead of the slowly liquidating farm liens. Many of the formerly gilt-edged agricultural mortgages became valueless when the high wages of the oil industry induced men to desert the plows for the drilling rigs. To meet the need for easily cashed securities, many bankers invested in the highly speculative promotional stocks of the oil industry.

The uncertainty of finding new pools prevented loans for wildcat wells from being good bank risks. Sometimes, too, the discoverer of such a reservoir of petroleum became a very hard-pressed operator struggling to protect his property. The cost of offsets would prevent the repayment of previous debts, and might even result in bankruptcy. Some of the producers quickly formed companies and sold stock, which of course was offered to the bankers. The promotional stock often proved quite disappointing to the investors. When a few of the oil-town banks became insolvent, a wave of skepticism swept over the others. Thus even legitimate loans were difficult for oil men to negotiate. By 1920, most of the banks had added oil men to their boards of directors for the better solution of the financial problems of the oil industry. Departments for the sale of oil securities were opened in a number of banks, and others even went so far as to promote petroleum firms. Some oil men, such as Harry F. Sinclair, became the virtual proprietors of banks. One of the significant reasons that Tulsa became an important center for the oil industry was the bankers' knowledge of the collateral value of leases, wells, and equipment. At one time the loans of the Tulsa banks to the petroleum industry were exceeded only by those of the financial institutions of New York City.

Equal to finances in importance and imperative in the urgency of its solution was the question of transportation at the newly found oil pools. More often than not, the discovery was in an inaccessible spot. The roads, if they existed at all, would be poor, and certainly not prepared for the great volume of heavy traffic necessary in the development of an oil pool. Generally the new wells would be far from a railway, which necessitated considerable hauling. During the early part of the century, teams of large horses and mules were used, although the bogginess of some sections of Louisiana made oxen preferable there. Later, trucks and tractors, supplanting teams, had the effect of churning the mud and dust as well as wrecking hard-surface highways.

Railroads, of course, were very desirable, and several of them were constructed in the Gulf-Southwest definitely as a result of oil discoveries. During the exploitation of the Cushing Pool, the Oil Belt Terminal Railroad was built to reduce the shipping distance from Tulsa. The remarkable Jake Hamon organized the Oklahoma, New Mexico, and Pacific Railroad at Ardmore and laid a line to Ringling during the heyday of the Healdton Pool. Later, when the Ranger and Burkburnett pools were at their height, Hamon organized the Wichita Falls, Ranger and Fort Worth Railroad, a project that the oil men heartily welcomed. A dramatic episode that displayed Hamon's initiative and efficiency occurred at Ranger during the construction of this road, which was sometimes known as the Hamon-Kell Road or the Oil Belt Railway. A court gave Hamon permission to cross an intersecting railway: two hundred laborers and twenty teams completed the crossing in a single day. A conception of the importance of the railroads may be acquired from the fact that in the year of 1919 the Ranger freight depot did more business than Dallas, Fort Worth, and New Orleans combined in the same period. Later, at Seminole, more than ten thousand cars were unloaded in four months. In addition to causing the construction of railways, the oil industry had another far-reaching effect in the construction or improvement of paved highways extending throughout the Gulf-Southwest.

Aside from the strength of this industry in supporting the development of mechanized agriculture, the petroleum of the Gulf-Southwest has directly affected farming. Of course, there were exceptions when the husbandmen objected to the drilling of oil wells in their wheat fields, but generally the opportunity to move to town and live on a royalty income was welcomed. There were occasions when the approach of the oil industry meant no more than a bonus of a few thousand dollars to the farmer, but with that money he acquired previously unknown comforts and luxuries. Rural children received better educational advantages which the pigs and cotton would not have provided. Some of the fathers gave their sons farms that were far better for agriculture than the homesteads of their parents. Scrub cattle were displaced by registered livestock, just as hired hands and mules were supplanted by tractors and other machinery.

By no means, however, was the influence of the petroleum industry always beneficial to agriculture. Thousands of acres of previously arable land became sterile when flooded with brine from near-by wells. At times, even, livestock was killed by the salty water. More serious—because the rains would in the course of time remove the salt—was the encouragement of tenancy which followed the spread of the oil pools. Considerable oil wealth went into the purchase of land, some of which was operated in the form of scientific farms. But much of the land had been acquired solely for its probable petroleum content, and consequently the owners permitted it to lie fallow. The correlation between the oil industry and the high percentage of tenancy in the eastern part of Oklahoma, the former Indian Territory, can hardly be denied. Between 1908 and 1920, when the oil industry was busiest in that area, the laws permitted the Indians to dispose of much of their land. Many of the Indians, unable to read or write and with no traditional understanding of private ownership of land, became rich from petroleum. They were the wards of the county courts, which appointed guardians to administer their expenditures and estates. Sometimes that process left the Indian poor and the guardian wealthy. Often the Indian was stripped of his land by trading it for a railroad ticket or a few dollars. In 1900, only about two-fifths of the farmers in Oklahoma

Social and Economic Influences

were tenants, whereas in 1935 61 per cent did not own the land they tilled. In thirteen of the state's counties, all petroleum-producing and in the former Indian Territory, tenancy amounted to more than 70 per cent. From the Texas ranchman to the Kansas wheat raiser, from the Creek Indian to the Acadian pepper grower, rural life has been altered by the petroleum industry.

Only their optimistic imaginations, often unsupported by experience, limited the boom-town citizens in the expenditure of public funds. Throughout the Gulf-Southwest, ghosts of once bustling little cities bear mute witness of the fallaciousness of human judgment. Some of them still are the homes of a few persons, others may be marked by abandoned buildings or only the stark concrete of a deserted bank vault. In the days of remarkable prosperity, municipal debts naturally accrued, but often far in excess of the city's future ability to pay. Several of the boom towns have had themselves legally declared bankrupt, or have considered that action.

A case in point is Earlsboro, Oklahoma. It was a tiny village until the Seminole oil-producing district was discovered near by. Soon more than seven thousand persons were getting mail at the General Delivery window in the post office, and one hundred thousand dollars was being invested in a modern hotel. Earlsboro then paved its streets, erected a school, and installed sewer and water systems. The flush period of the oil pool passed, causing a rapid decline in the town's population and taxable valuation. Ten years later, in 1938, the bonded debt of Earlsboro was $169,000, and the property within the city limits was valued at only $199,000. The officials gave up and did not levy a tax. A petition in bankruptcy, later sustained by the United States Supreme Court, was filed in the Federal District Court at Oklahoma City.

The cultural transition of the Gulf-Southwest has also produced strange conditions as a result of the merging, and fluctuating fortunes, of representatives of all parts of the United States. Eastern college graduates married quarter-blood Indian girls, and the daughters of wealthy Texas ranchmen became the wives of sturdy sons of Pennsylvania coal miners. Chippendale cabinets occupied space in homes which sorely needed painting. Sons and daughters of ambitious parents drove their own automobiles to the resorts in New Jersey and Massachusetts, where they sometimes developed a feeling of unwarranted superiority toward their fathers. Music, art, literature, and architecture have received an impetus from the oil industry which has produced notable accomplishments. World-famous concert musicians have appeared before large and appreciative audiences in the major cities. Artists, many of them native to the region, have pictured derricks and boom-town scenes. Novelists, in some instances from personal experience, have told stories of the oil country. From modest homes to mansions, from skyscrapers to churches, from simple pleasures to more effete living—a new world was constructed at Tulsa. With all its contradictions, the general cultural level has been raised to a wholesomely critical point.

Every individual throughout the oil-producing region, and almost everyone living in the entire United States, for that matter, has been affected directly by the taxation of the oil industry. In the Gulf-Southwest, the revenue has taken a multitude of forms varying from charges on production to fees for processing. School districts, towns, counties, and states have instituted special levies. Some of the accruing funds have been legally designated for particular purposes, such as the support of schools or the construction of highways, while others have been consumed in the general operation of the government. The largest single source

of income in the six states of this study has been the petroleum industry, which in some of the commonwealths
has produced as much as half of the total revenue.

With such a large share of the public funds coming from
the industry, it was a foregone conclusion that the leading
oil men would take a personal interest in political life.
Young men in the state legislatures sometimes came from
the legal departments of the larger companies, and in many
cases the executives of the oil firms were close advisers of
the governors. Three important men in the industry—Ross
Sterling in Texas, E. W. Marland in Oklahoma, and Alfred
Landon in Kansas—rose to the position of governor in their
respective states. Many men connected with the oil business have occupied lesser political positions. There has been
corruption, but surprisingly little has become known, con-
sidering the billions of dollars in wealth that the industry
has produced.

At least one city, Tulsa, has been the distinct creation of
the petroleum industry, with the history of which it is in-
separably connected. The building of the city followed the
discovery of many oil pools within a radius of one hundred
miles. When oil was first discovered at Red Fork in 1901,
Tulsa, in the trees across the Arkansas river, was a hamlet
of about one thousand people. As the years passed, petroleum was found in all directions and the town grew with
immense and consistent strides, largely because of the
hotel built to accommodate the men with operations in the
Glenn Pool, to the south. Northward, toward Kansas, a
series of smaller and less spectacular pools came into being,
yet operations still could be conducted from Tulsa. Then
the internationally important Cushing Pool was discovered
in 1912 about fifty miles to the west. By 1920, reservoirs
of petroleum on all sides had been exploited from Tulsa,
which was becoming a center for refining and shipping the

product. Factories there were busy producing equipment and machinery for the petroleum industry. By 1940, Tulsa had a population of about 150,000 cosmopolitan residents, most of whom were connected, at least indirectly, with the petroleum industry. Tulsa people, many of whom were born in Pennsylvania, have boasted that the city contains more millionaires than any other city of comparable size in the world. Some of the owners of its numerous costly residences commute by plane to their oil properties in New Mexico and the Texas Panhandle.

Just as thoroughly an oil town as Tulsa, but with cheap marine transportation to assist its development, is Beaumont, Texas. Since the day in 1901 when Anthony F. Lucas completed the first artesian oil well a few miles from the little town, Beaumont has been an important refining and exporting center for the petroleum industry. Millions of dollars have been invested in refineries and ship-loading equipment there. It is not a large city, but it forms the business center for the world's largest refining district. Another city on the Gulf Coast of Texas, Houston, owes a great deal of its size and importance to the oil business. Houston is not essentially a development of the petroleum business, but it became a port through the dredging of a fifty-mile canal from Galveston, and along this waterway several important refineries have been put into operation.

All the world has felt the influence of the oil industry of the Gulf-Southwest, with tankers taking crude petroleum around Florida to refineries on the Atlantic seaboard and in Europe. Two of the companies that were born at Spindletop, the Texas Company and the Gulf Oil Corporation, have circled the globe with their holdings. Several of the other southwestern firms have become nationally significant. The large companies are integrated so as to control all the steps of the business from the leases and pipe lines to the refineries and retail outlets. The retailing of gasoline through company-owned stations has made the motorist familiar with the same signs and trademarks from California to Maine, and some of those same insignia have become known in Europe and Asia.

The industry's strength has built towns and cities, whose residents have been more comfortable because gas has been available for heating and cooking. It has both inaugurated and improved education, and has changed the courses of study. Political life and government have felt the weight of the revenues gained through taxation of oil property. Business, religion, the arts, and farming have not escaped the dynamic power of the money and products of petroleum. Possibly, however, its most important influence has been the spirit of speculative daring that has permeated the minds of many persons born and reared where a man could become wealthy in a day.

Legal Aspects

POSSIBLY the legal aspects of the very complex oil industry have become the most involved and difficult division of the business. When the young industry had few complications, the laws were simple. As the extraction and processing of petroleum became more scientific and intricate, the laws also passed through a transitional period which produced problems in enforcement that were technical.

The laws of the final decade of the last century dealt with such relatively simple matters as the proper casing and plugging of wells. A Kansas act in 1891 required the use of casing to prevent the intrusion of water into the oil-bearing formations. At that time the chief commercial product of petroleum was kerosene, hence the statutes fixed standards for that fuel.

The activities of the oil industry at Corsicana in 1899 caused the enactment in Texas of a law stipulating the conditions under which gas might be freed. It was in 1905 that the amount of gas to be produced with petroleum first was limited in the future state of Oklahoma. The gas was to be freed if it was less valuable than the oil that was produced, according to that law. A decline in the price of petroleum resulted in the passage of four militant and drastic laws in Kansas that same year. Two associations of Kansas oil men were formed for the purpose of seeking legislation, and the acts were passed. One, later declared to be unconstitutional, provided for the erection of a state-owned refinery. Another made the pipe lines in Kansas common carriers. A third measure fixed a maximum fee for the pipe-line transportation of petroleum; and the fourth law was known as the "Anti-Discrimination Bill." Their efforts at fostering legislation a success, the Kansas oil men continued to urge, through their associations, a reduction in the output of petroleum and an increase in consumption.

After the enactment in 1909 of the common purchaser and common carrier act applying to pipe lines, the Oklahoma Legislature in 1915 passed an epochal measure. By that time, two great Oklahoma oil pools had wrecked the prices of crude oil on different occasions, so a new element was introduced into the legal structure. The law marked the beginning of economic legislation, limiting the yield to the market demand. A part of the regulations, never enforced, prohibited the sale of petroleum below the cost of production. The meaning of waste was extended to include underground loss. The acts were written with the assistance of Federal experts at a time when producers in the Healdton Pool were crying for relief from thirty-cent oil. At Tulsa a meeting of oil men discussed the new measures and avowed that the Oklahoma Corporation Commission, authorized to enforce the laws, would soon discover that saving both gas and petroleum was impossible. Some of the men said that the measures were radical and would be impossible to enforce.

Two years later, in Kansas, a lobby of oil men again demonstrated its strength when stringent revenue measures were proposed in the legislature. It was suggested that the state require a license fee of ten dollars for every well drilled, whether oil, gas, or nothing at all was discovered in the hole. In addition, a tax of three cents a barrel on petroleum and an equal amount on each thousand cubic feet of gas was proposed. These measures would have yielded revenue for the state, but the oil men succeeded in preventing their enactment.

In 1919 the expansion of the Burkburnett Pool into the bed of the Red River brought about a legal battle, with military aspects, between Oklahoma and Texas. When the Texas oil operators began to erect derricks and drill holes in the bed of the river, the state of Oklahoma sued Texas. Under the Federal mining laws, Oklahomans filed claims on the river bed, and there they discovered petroleum. When the famous Rangers were sent by Texas to police and control its land, Oklahoma retaliated by sending the state militia to uphold its claims. It was the contention of Oklahoma officials that the bed of the river belonged to that state by virtue of the treaty of the United States with Spain in 1819, one hundred years before. Texans agreed that the Treaty of 1819 had fixed the river as the boundary, but argued that the line between the two states had never been definitely settled. A Supreme Court decision (162 U. S. 27) in 1895 had fixed the boundary of Texas as the south bank of the Red River, a decree that had given Greer County to Oklahoma. That opinion had been based on the Treaty of 1819 with Spain. The Oklahoma officials called attention to the decision and declared emphatically that the line was the south bank of the river. The important question thus required the delineation of the south bank of the Red River in the year of 1819, and the flooding and shifting character of the river made the problem most difficult to decide. Texas officials believed that the river had not flooded the oil-producing valley on its south side in more than one hundred years.

Frederick A. Delano, of Chicago, appointed as receiver for the Federal government, took control of the disputed area. He took possession of about 170 producing oil wells in the area. In 1921 the United States Supreme Court decided that the claims of Texas to the southern side of the flood channel were justified. Then the state of Oklahoma claimed the land of the actual river bed on the theory that the Red River was navigable. When the question of navigability was raised, the Federal government filed a brief in which it was argued that the land of the river bed belonged to the Indians. The government claimed that the Red River never had been navigable above the Kiamichi Mountains in eastern Oklahoma. Again in 1923 the Supreme Court wrote a decision regarding the river, this time giving the bed of the stream to the United States. Little petroleum was ever discovered beneath the bed of the Red River.

The bed of the Arkansas River, one of the boundaries of the Osage Reservation, was also the subject of a legal controversy, this time between the Indians and Oklahoma. The state contended that the Arkansas was a navigable stream and therefore its bed was the property of Oklahoma. The Indians claimed the bed of the stream on the theory that it was not subject to navigation. The case was decided in a Federal District Court in Oklahoma, the Osages receiving half of the disputed land. Their share was worth about twenty-five million dollars.

By 1920, the men in the oil industry in Texas were so annoyed by the activities of that state's legislature in giving the Railroad Commission control of the business that they jestingly objected. They believed some other industry should have legislative attention, so they proposed that laws be passed to prevent blizzards from injuring the cattle on the ranges in winter. The protesters suggested that laws should specify the proper planting of corn and the correct chopping of cotton. Jokesters were busy in Oklahoma, too, in 1931, when Governor William H. Murray asked for a

tax of five cents a gallon on gasoline. Along the highways
they placed placards declaring that "Gasoline is 5c, but we
must have another 5c for Governor Bill."

An antitrust act in Texas proved impotent in the 1930's
when it was taken before the courts in a suit instituted by
Attorney General James V. Allred. Penalties amounting to
seventeen million dollars were sought in a case against
fifteen major oil companies, the Texas Petroleum Marketers' Association, and the American Petroleum Institute.
The decision of the court in 1933 stated that the National
Industrial Recovery Act superseded the Texas law, and
that consequently Allred's suit had no basis. The case was
appealed by the state, but two years later the Third Circuit
Court of Appeals declared the Texas antitrust law to be
unconstitutional, thus concluding the suit.

In 1935 the Texas gas industry became the subject of
legislation and litigation when the legislature enacted a
measure to give the Railroad Commission regulatory authority. By the gas conservation act the Railroad Commission was authorized to prorate the production of gas
and to force the gas pipe lines to take the output of the
small producing companies. The resulting litigation reached
the Federal courts in 1936. A Circuit Court decision held
the law to be unconstitutional, on the ground that the proration orders, which forced the pipe-line companies to buy
the gas of small producers even when they themselves
owned a sufficient supply, had the effect of taking property
without due process of law.

One of the most embracing cases of antitrust litigation
developed in 1936 when the gasoline jobbers of several mid-
western states complained to the Federal government. An
investigation was started in April, and in July it resulted
in the indictment at Madison, Wisconsin, of more than
twenty large oil companies, three publishers, and more

than fifty important executives in the industry. They were charged with conspiracy to raise and fix the price of gasoline. The Federal government accused the indicted persons and firms of having organized a system through which gasoline was purchased at spot prices from the independent refineries in the enormous East Texas district, Oklahoma, and elsewhere. Gasoline could be purchased there for less than four cents a gallon. Then, the prosecution charged, the gasoline was distributed to jobbers on long-term contracts at prices that were published in the trade periodicals.

The accused companies sold 85 per cent of the gasoline consumed in the states of Michigan, Minnesota, Wisconsin, North Dakota, South Dakota, Iowa, Indiana, Missouri, and Kansas. The trial was conducted at Madison because that city was in the area in which consumers were affected. Legal preliminaries were completed, and the trial was started in June, 1937.

A large part of one of the business buildings of Madison was rented and equipped as headquarters for the defendants and their attorneys. The completeness of the establishment was indicated by the fact that a switchboard with fifteen outside trunk wires was installed, in addition to thirty-eight interoffice telephones. The trial was conducted in a room that had been constructed to accommodate two hundred persons, but on this occasion it was expected to hold more than ninety attorneys, forty-six defendants, newspapermen, and a jury panel of eighty.

The defense of the oil men and companies was based on the "reasonableness" of their operations. They contended that their activities were justified by the code that had been placed in effect by the National Recovery Administration. One man even said that Harold Ickes, Secretary of the Department of the Interior, should be indicted because he had been the administrator of the oil industry under the authority of the Recovery Act. The Federal attorneys objected to the use of the word "reasonable," and avowed that the accused men and firms had taken the law into their own hands. They asserted that the code had been nullified in May, 1935, but that the conspiracy had started in March and had continued through 1936.

The court gradually dismissed the charges against persons and companies until only sixteen companies and thirty persons remained accused when a decision was rendered in January, 1938. These defendants were convicted and assessed penalties of fines and jail terms. Motions for new trials were filed and argued. Another pause in the case came in May, 1940, when the United States Supreme Court upheld the conviction of twelve companies and five persons. Rehearing of the case was denied on June 3, 1940.

Possibly by far the most important element in the legal history of the Southwest's oil industry has been the development of administrative law. The nature of the industry lent itself particularly to a control that was pliable and could be adjusted readily to changing conditions. Oklahoma led the way in 1915 when it placed the administration of the industry in the hands of the Corporation Commission. The Corporation Commission was authorized to make rules for the conduct of the industry, with appeals from its decisions going directly to the Supreme Court of the state. A virtue of this system of control was the fact that the regulatory body might employ technically and scientifically trained persons to assist in the administration. That element was offset, however, by the fact that the industry might gain undue influence through its ready willingness to supply the necessary specialized knowledge. Texas, in 1919, followed Oklahoma when it placed the Railroad Commission in charge of its oil industry. The action of Texas was inspired by the great Ranger and Burkburnett pools. In 1923, soon after the discovery of the El Dorado and Smackover pools within its boundaries, Arkansas set up a regulatory office with the state geologist in charge. The Arkansas control declined, however, after the flush period of its two great pools had passed, not to be revived until the development of the tristate Rodessa Pool. Before 1936, the states of Louisiana, Arkansas, Kansas, and New Mexico had also instituted regulatory bodies to administer the oil industry.

In the administration of the industry the regulatory boards had been forced to struggle with several problems, some of which had been settled. The indefinite phrase, "reasonable market demand," acquired a definite meaning, which was, "current consumptive demand." The boards or commissions were expected to regulate such matters as the spacing of wells, the allowables of pools and the wells within them, the gas-oil ratio of production, the share of each operator in the oil, gas, and reservoir energy of the pool. The state agency might authorize the pooling of properties for unit operation, or it might even have the authority to compel unitization. Hearings of men in the industry were conducted and became the basis for the regulations. Broadly speaking, it had been recognized by 1940 that the state could govern the production of oil and gas through its police powers. Most of the statutes had been upheld by the courts as constitutional. Questions that had been settled definitely included the right of the state to prevent the waste of a natural resource, its right to govern production, and its obligation to let each operator produce his fair share.

The Specter of Governmental Control

SINCE 1861, when it first felt the sharp pains of over-production, the oil industry has labored under the ever recurrent specter of governmental control. For many years the industry operated its wells by the "rule of capture," which meant that the petroleum became the property of the person who took it from the earth. Oil was likened to migrating birds, which belonged to the hunter who snared or killed them. The practical application of the rule of capture often caused the competitive drilling of wells in large numbers. This not only drained the petroleum rapidly from beneath the driller's own land, but was calculated to draw some from below his neighbor's. Such a system of operation was certain to result periodically—when such large pools as Cushing were found—in great overproduction. This condition in turn depressed the price, and often a large amount of petroleum was stored wastefully in earthen or poorly constructed steel tanks. Those two factors aroused dissatisfaction in the industry and incited public discussion of the waste of a natural resource. State and Federal governments alike were interested in preventing the waste of such a resource as petroleum, and on these occasions the specter of governmental control loomed large.

A new scheme of production, however, known as proration, was introduced in 1915 when the industry in Oklahoma was harassed by the output of the great Cushing and

Healdton pools. Proration means the dividing of the permitted production between the different pools as well as between the several operators in each pool. It is the antithesis of the rule of capture, which permitted an operator to take all the petroleum he could get, even when his neighbor was unable to remove any. The equitable fixing of the allowables of pools and wells became technical, and involved consideration of acreage, gas pressure, bottom-hole pressure, and other questions that sometimes varied with the different pools. For years proration was applied only with the intention of keeping production at a point within the capacity of the pipe lines to move the oil. As the early efforts of the Oklahoma Corporation Commission to restrict the production of the Cushing Pool were nullified by the courts, even the reduction to pipe-line capacity was delayed as a system of operation. The distress that resulted from the great production of the Cushing and Healdton pools aroused the desire to control the output of the wells for the purpose of raising the price. The Oklahoma Corporation Commission therefore attempted to fix the price at a profitable level, claiming the authority to do so under the provision of the law which made "economic waste" illegal.

It was during the First World War, in 1917, that the legislature of Texas gave the Railroad Commission the authority to regulate the petroleum industry. The next year Louisiana recognized underground waste in its legal structure. At this time the Federal government, because of the war, became especially interested in fuel for airplanes and ships, so 1918 is looked on as the beginning of the movement for national control of the industry.

The immense flush production of the Burkburnett Pool urgently attracted attention in 1918 when the price of crude oil dropped from $3.25 to $1.90 a barrel. The Texas Legislature passed conservation acts, but they were too vaguely

181

written to be effective. Oil operators of Wichita County held a mass meeting at Wichita Falls in 1919, requesting the Texas Railroad Commission to close the wells at Burkburnett for thirty days so that the pipe lines might transport the petroleum from the pool. The Railroad Commission had investigated the conditions in near-by Eastland County, and had found that the waste of gas alone exceeded one hundred thousand dollars a day on twenty leases in one pool. Thus the first proration order in Texas dealt, by request, with an extension of the Burkburnett Pool. The order closed the wells for thirty days, but it never was effective because it expired before the details were arranged; and in the meantime additional pipe lines were completed to move all the oil. The wells of the townsite division of the Burkburnett Pool had become so numerous that in 1919 the Federal Fuel Conservation Board took control of the area and limited the drilling. The Federal officials permitted one well on each city lot, and limited the storage of each to one thousand barrels in underground tanks.

Texas oil men got a quiet but hearty laugh out of a public announcement by one energetic member of the Railroad Commission in 1919. This individual made a quick trip through the area of oil production and then declared that the regulatory body had already saved the state fifty-five million dollars. The humor of such exaggeration was not lost on the industry, for only two hundred thousand dollars worth of petroleum had been produced. Actually the Railroad Commission was confronted with such a serious problem in regulating the industry that in distress it appealed to the oil men for aid. The Gulf Coast Producers Association and the Mid-Continent Oil and Gas Association were asked to assist the Railroad Commission by the selection of three producers from each Texas pool to act as an advisory committee. The committees from the different pools were expected to aid in writing rules for the control of the industry. These rules were as vague and indefinite as the statutes, and gave some persons the impression that they were designed to apply only to the small operators. The three members of the Railroad Commission not only were very busy, but were handicapped by their lack of familiarity with the petroleum industry. Also, the latter was well equipped with attorneys, technicians, and scientific data. Its leaders generously agreed to assist in the enforcement of the rules, laying a foundation for the belief that the oil men controlled the organization that was authorized to regulate them.

Following those events in Texas, the Oklahoma Corporation Commission issued an order designed to delay the drilling of the Hewitt Pool because of lack of facilities to transport its production. The oil men, however, failed to co-operate with the commission, and instead tried to institute a system of control through voluntary agreement. The American Petroleum Institute, meeting at St. Louis in 1922, heard an expression of fear that Federal control would follow the "rising tide of socialistic doctrine and state regulation." It was hoped that the American Petroleum Institute might succeed in co-ordinating the industry, and that organization tried to persuade twelve thousand small operators to curtail their production. Arguments for a reduction in output had little effect on the wanton flush production of the El Dorado and Smackover pools in Arkansas, but the state legislature enacted an oil and gas conservation law in 1923.

Important events followed a parallel course in Oklahoma and Texas in 1926, when the prolific Seminole and Yates pools were discovered. In Oklahoma the oil men appealed to the Corporation Commission, while in Texas the assistance of the Railroad Commission was sought. The operators in the Yates Pool organized themselves and planned a system of voluntary proration, but they feared that their agreement might be considered a conspiracy in restraint of trade. They went, therefore, to the Texas Railroad Commission, which gave them official sanction in the form of an order placing the proration agreement in force.

A more involved development took place in the case of Seminole. Some of the operators of that pool conferred at Tulsa and planned a curtailment in production. They employed Ray Collins, who, as a privately paid umpire, issued orders that were designed to reduce drilling and production. Difficulties arose, however, from the fact that not all the Seminole operators had agreed that Collins should regulate the pool. The Oklahoma Corporation Commission ordered that the Seminole Pool should not produce more oil than the pipe lines could move, but the output became a rising flood.

At Washington, the Federal Oil Conservation Board, which had been created by President Calvin Coolidge, inquired into the situation that was developing in the industry. Henry L. Doherty, one of the nation's important oil men, argued that the Federal government had the right to control the petroleum industry just as it did the munitions business. Charles Evans Hughes, then attorney for the American Petroleum Institute, answered that conservation was a state matter and not a problem of the national government. Herbert Hoover, Secretary of the Department of Commerce, avowed that in his opinion the American Petroleum Institute should use its energy to modify the Sherman Antitrust Law. Walter C. Teagle, one of the oil industry's most influential executives, expressed the idea that a flood of oil would always be possible until there was co-operation; hence he wanted the laws changed to permit unified action within the industry.

The Specter of Governmental Control

By 1928 some persons believed that the oil industry needed a plan of co-operation, a conclusion they reached on the assumption that it was unable to solve its own problems. These persons thought that the state and Federal governments should try to assist the industry, possibly with some sort of unit control system. President Coolidge wanted to lend the assistance of the Federal government. His plan, requiring a scientific study, would have involved the American Petroleum Institute, the United States Geological Survey, and specialists from the staffs of several schools. The Federal Oil Conservation Board suggested that the members of the industry enter voluntary co-operative agreements for the control of different pools, and further recommended that the states enact laws that would endorse the legality of such agreements.

The Federal Trade Commission wanted to be of assistance to the petroleum industry, and in 1927 it issued a booklet entitled *Prices, Profits, and Competition in the Petroleum Industry*. The booklet stressed the need of control to protect the supply of oil and the investments in the industry. The Oil Conservation Board had studied, with the aid of technical advisers, the responsibility of the Federal government, but it had been given no power to remove the petroleum industry from the jurisdiction of the anti-trust laws. In general, the board had a kindly attitude toward the industry.

The chiefs of five of the nation's largest oil companies, all of whom were interested in the big Seminole Pool, had conferred at New York in May, 1927, and had become a committee to plan the proration of the great Oklahoma oil-producing district. They, for a second time, employed Ray Collins to act as umpire in the regulation of the area, and he asked the Oklahoma Corporation Commission to give official status to his orders. The commission complied with

185

the request, thus placing a privately paid official in administrative control. Collins limited the daily output of the Seminole district to 450,000 barrels, a total that he divided among the different operators. The Seminole producers considered the proration a means of balancing supply and demand.

Several conclusions, important to the industry, were the result of restricting the oil wells to pipe-line capacity. It was found that the restriction not only failed to injure the well but actually delayed the intrusion of water. Choked wells produced longer, and since the reservoir energy was retained, the expensive process of artificial lifting was delayed.

In Texas, in 1928, two more requests were made for the assistance of the Railroad Commission in pool proration. The Hendrick Pool, in Winkler County, was the second pool to be limited at the request of the oil operators. The third was the Robert Settles, in Howard and Glasscock counties. Here, as at the Yates Pool, the effort of the officials was to limit the output to the demand.

The first proration in Kansas occurred in 1929 when the prolific Ritz-Canton, Greenwick, and Voshell pools were discovered in the western part of the state. The proration there was similar in development to previous instances in Oklahoma and Texas, being a voluntary agreement of the operators to limit the wells to the available pipe-line capacity. In New Mexico that same year the operators of the new Hobbs Pool conferred with officials to plan a proration program.

Two proposals to exercise control over the oil industry were placed before Federal officials in 1929. The president of the American Petroleum Institute, E. B. Reeser, named a committee that included oil men of Oklahoma, Kansas, Texas, Arkansas, Louisiana, and New Mexico. The committee recommended that the Federal and state laws be changed so as to permit unit pool operation and allow agreements for the purpose of reducing production. Such alterations of the statutes would have nullified the anti-trust laws of the United States; consequently Attorney General Mitchell frowned on the suggestions. The other effort in this direction consisted of two laws proposed by the conservation committee of the minerals section of the American Bar Association. One of these laws would have permitted voluntary co-operation, while the other would have provided for co-operation by means of coercion.

By this time the oil industry generally agreed that the purpose of proration was price stabilization, but in the courts it was necessary to defend the program on the basis of conservation. In June, 1929, President Herbert Hoover called a conference of the governors of the oil-producing states for the purpose of discussing conservation. The conference met at Colorado Springs, and Mark L. Requa, formerly director of the oil division of the United States Fuel Administration, became chairman. Delegates were present from Oklahoma, Texas, California, Kansas, Colorado, New Mexico, Utah, and Wyoming, but they were officially without power and nothing definite was accomplished. The meeting resulted, however, in showing the cleavage that existed between the interests of the major and minor companies.

Wirt Franklin, of Healdton Pool fame, became the leader of the minor companies. They organized the Independent Petroleum Association of America, which became an aggressive institution. These companies protested that no legal reduction of the domestic production should be instituted as long as foreign petroleum was imported without duty. They argued that the major concerns would be able to injure the small firms by means of prorating the output in this country while at the same time importing Venezuelan oil. The Independent Petroleum Association began a fight that culminated in 1932 in the enactment of a tariff on foreign petroleum.

Most of the state laws in 1930, and afterwards, were designed to foster the stabilization of the industry. The term "conservation" was used loosely. Some persons even said that higher prices for petroleum would aid society in general. The Mid-Continent Royalty Owners Association, with members in all the southwestern states except New Mexico, acknowledged the value of proration, despite the fact that it might be construed as "restraint of trade."

The politico-economic expansion of proration in Texas was rapid in 1930, the leaders of the industry organizing the Central Proration Committee and volunteering to assist the Railroad Commission. Rules were written, a state over-seer for the industry was appointed, and umpires for the different pools were selected. In nine years the price of petroleum had declined from $3.50 to $1.00 a barrel. The Railroad Commission issued the first state-wide proration order in August, but C. M. Joiner completed his portentous Daisy Bradford No. 3 in October, and the development of the herculean East Texas Pool had begun. The Railroad Commission permitted the expansion.

The swift development of the East Texas Pool was pos-sible through exceptions to Rule 37, a spacing regulation that had been adopted in 1919 by the Railroad Commission. In substance, the rule provided that no well might be drilled within 300 feet of another producing hole, or closer than 150 feet to a lease line; but exceptions could be granted for protecting vested interests and preventing waste. The intention was to prevent pepperbox drilling. Much of the land in the area—forty miles long—that constituted East Texas consisted of small farms and town lots. Strict enforcement of Rule 37 would have limited the number of wells, and in some tracts would even have prevented drilling. Generally Rule 37 had the support of the major companies and the large leaseholders, while the minor companies and the small landowners objected to it. About 65 per cent of the twenty-six thousand wells in the East Texas Pool were drilled as exceptions to Rule 37.

Out of the growth of this fabulous pool came the first serious questioning of the authority of the Railroad Commission to limit production in conformity with market demand. The economic interests of the operators obviously affected their attitudes on the question. The larger companies wanted a limitation of production for the protection of their far-flung assets. Other men and companies, with no properties outside of the East Texas Pool, wanted their wells to produce at the maximum rate so that they might enjoy their properties to the fullest extent immediately. Although the smaller operators wanted the highest possible prices, they were willing, and could afford, to sell oil at a lower price than the big firms. The power of the Railroad Commission to limit production was sustained by the Austin Court of Civil Appeals in 1932, on the grounds that the regulation prevented the waste of reservoir pressure in the pool and that it tended to reduce the economic loss by production in excess of the market demand. That decision was supported by the United States Supreme Court in a similar case in Oklahoma.

A second legal conflict of interests that became important in the thirties in the East Texas Pool dealt with the method of allocating the well allowables. Again the attitudes of the operators were dictated by their economic interests. Although the first method of allocation to suggest itself was that of giving each well the same allowable, there were many objections and counterproposals. The per-well allowable,

189

which permitted equal production from all holes, was fought on the ground that it did not consider the differences in productive capacities, large and small landholdings, the ratio of oil and gas being produced, thickness of the producing formations, and the variations in the amount of petroleum beneath the different leases. Various formulas for fixing allocations were suggested. Generally the operator wanted the particular type of allocation that would be the most advantageous to his property. The early per-well allowables were stricken by judicial decisions in the East Texas litigation. The per-well system of allocation doubtless encouraged the drilling of more wells, and a slight advantage was given to the better producers.

An extraordinary amount of litigation sprang from the administration of the East Texas Pool, where in 1931 some operators believed that the state would be unable to exercise control. The Railroad Commission attempted to follow a policy of restraint suggested by the Central Proration Committee, but injunctions interfered. At that time the oil wells of the Gulf Coast were permitted to flow at their maximum rate, for there a market was available. The operators in East Texas avowed that they also had a ready market, although they were willing to accept a smaller price. The Railroad Commission attempted to settle the argument by raising the allowable of the East Texas Pool from fifty thousand to ninety thousand barrels a day. Then the Central Proration Committee threatened to cease co-operating with the officials. Operators in the pool organized themselves and prepared to fight for their interests. The result of this turmoil was that by June, 1931, the posted price of petroleum dropped to twenty cents a barrel, and some spot sales at two cents were reported.

In August, 1931, when oil was selling for thirteen cents a barrel in East Texas and eighteen in Oklahoma, Governor

William H. Murray closed the flush pools of Oklahoma by martial law. Governor Ross Sterling soon followed Murray's action by sending the militia to East Texas. Many oil men looked on the East Texas Pool as the arch enemy of the industry.

The declaration of martial law and the presence of Texas troops tended to increase the price of East Texas petroleum. The receipt of more money for less oil caused land and royalty owners to cease objecting to curtailed production. The operators, however, early in 1932 asked a United States Circuit Court judge for an injunction against martial law. The court, later upheld by the United States Supreme Court, granted the injunction with the opinion that the militia could not be used to enforce proration. Governor Sterling replied that the militia was in East Texas to keep the peace, but that it also would prevent the oil from upsetting the national market. The judge commented that the only "riot" was that of the oil men trying to produce more petroleum.

Federal interference in the affairs of the East Texas Pool took definite and active form in 1933 when, after the passage of the National Industrial Recovery Act, President Franklin D. Roosevelt signed an executive order prohibiting the interstate and export shipment of oil illegally produced. Much oil was being produced in excess of the legal allowables, so at the suggestion of the Independent Petroleum Association a special office of the Federal Bureau of Investigation was established at Longview. Under the Code of Fair Competition for the petroleum industry, Harold Ickes, Secretary of the Department of the Interior, took charge of the administration of the business. A. D. Ryan was sent to Texas by the Department of Justice to direct the administration of the code, and the operators organized the Texas Petroleum Council to assist him. Through the operation of the code an effort was made to balance supply and demand, but the rapid increase of the East Texas output caused the price there to fall to ten cents a barrel.

Fifty-five refineries had been constructed in the East Texas Field, and twenty-five of them were forced to close because they could not make a profit. Ten men were arrested in 1934 on charges of processing petroleum that had been illegally produced, and more federal officers were detailed to the enforcement work in the district. Each month the refineries in the big pool produced about ten million gallons of gasoline, which trucks moved to retailers in many parts of the United States. This cheaper gasoline resulted in many retail price wars throughout the central part of the country.

With the intention of controlling the flood of "hot oil," the Federal Tender Board was established in East Texas in October, 1934. It was the duty of that organization to investigate the source of all petroleum, then to issue tenders for its transportation if it had been produced in compliance with Texas laws. The Federal Tender Board was credited with reducing the production of illegal petroleum from 130,000 barrels to 5,000 barrels a day. Inspectors and minor officials were required throughout the pool. Often the discovery of illegal production, or the men who were responsible for it, was quite difficult. There was one instance in which a pipe line had been tapped and a connection made to a near-by well. Where the pipe line passed a refinery, it had been tapped again and a connection made to take oil to the plant. An investigation, however, failed to reveal the guilty persons. The Federal Tender Board ceased to operate in 1935 when the United States Supreme Court invalidated the National Industrial Recovery Act.

Interstate co-operation was significantly indicated when the governors of Oklahoma, Kansas, and Texas agreed to limit the production in their respective states. Ray Lyman Wilbur, then Secretary of the Interior, had suggested in a speech before the Independent Petroleum Association that the oil-producing states sign a treaty of co-operation. The tariff act of 1932 reduced the importation of petroleum by one-fourth, an achievement which increased the feeling that the states could control production by acting in unison. Another factor in the movement toward interstate co-operation was the Oil States Advisory Committee, which included representatives of the six southwestern commonwealths and Ohio, Colorado, Wyoming, and California. By 1932 an effort to stabilize the industry was being carried on through a program that had three chief features. First, engineers and economists forecast the demand for petroleum. Then the Oil States Advisory Committee fixed each state's share of the probable consumption. Third, the regulatory bodies in the different states were expected to prorate the oil pools so as to produce the suggested quotas. In 1933 the United States Bureau of Mines began estimating the demand for petroleum, a service which was started at the instance of Oklahoma oil men who wanted the information as an aid in determining proration quotas.

Three plans for co-ordinating supply and demand had been proposed by 1933. Henry L. Doherty had suggested Federal control. The American Petroleum Institute had outlined a scheme, to be world-wide in scope, for voluntary agreements within the industry. The third proposal, first made in 1910 by Elihu Root, intended to co-ordinate the industry through interstate agreements. Litigation had established two bases for state regulation of the industry; one rested on the correlative rights of the owners of an oil pool, the other on the authority to protect a natural resource. In 1933 Representative Tom McKeown, of Oklahoma, introduced in Congress a bill to authorize the oil-producing states to sign a compact, thus co-ordinating their efforts to regulate the industry. The objectives of the compact were to be the creation of a fact-finding body and commitment of the states to abide by the scientifically fixed production quotas. State authority, by that time, had been exerted to control one well, a single pool, and an entire state. The Code of Fair Competition became effective in September, 1933, when rules were made for the oil industry. The operation of the code, under the administration of Secretary Ickes, aroused objections within the industry, as it appeared to be a step toward complete Federal control.

The authority of the national government would bring new problems to the industry, whereas state control had been induced to take a well-recognized form. The fundamental features of proration had included the organization of a central control committee of oil men; the amount of petroleum that could be sold had been determined, then allocated between the different pools of the state; the regulatory bodies had accepted the allowables and given them the force of laws. Thus the authority of the state had rested on the co-operation of the oil industry itself.

Late in 1934 a congressional committee, studying the oil industry, toured the southwestern states. Hearings were conducted in several cities, and the important flush pools were visited. At Dallas, a mass meeting was held to discuss the illegal production of petroleum in the East Texas area. In Washington, Senator Elmer Thomas and Representative Wesley Disney, both of Oklahoma, placed an oil-control bill before Congress. Texans, even members of the legislature, believing that the measure would give the Federal government too much authority over the industry, succeeded in preventing the passage of the Thomas-Disney bill. Secretary Ickes, speaking before the American Petroleum Institute, discussed the possibility of making the petroleum in-

Oklahoma City discovery well; the Indian Territory Illuminating Oil Company's Foster No. 1, coming in December 4, 1928

An oil boom town; Necessity, Texas

Rotary rig boiler installation in the swamps of Louisiana

dustry a public utility. At the same convention the oil men heard one of their own leaders speak on the nationalization of the industry. Sir Henri Deterding, head of the huge Royal Dutch Shell Oil Company, avowed that the effects of the flood of East Texas production were felt throughout the world. It was his opinion that control of this single district, which at its peak yielded more than one-fifth of the world's output, was vital to international stabilization of the petroleum industry.

As the pressure for national control of the oil industry increased, Governor Marland, of Oklahoma, invited the chief executives of the other oil-producing states to a conference at his home at Ponca City. That meeting, in the Christmas season of 1934, was the first in a series which resulted in the writing of the Interstate Oil Compact. The Ponca City conference was followed in January, 1935, by the decision of the United States Supreme Court invalidating the National Industrial Recovery Act, thus removing Federal restrictions from the East Texas producers. Soon afterwards Congress passed the Connally "Hot Oil" Act. A second meeting of governors or their representatives was held at Dallas in February, 1935, to consider the Interstate Oil Compact. At the Dallas meeting a treaty was signed by representatives of Oklahoma, Texas, New Mexico, and California. Two important problems, the illegal production of the East Texas area and the growing size of the Rodessa Pool, faced the oil industry in the Southwest.

The congressional committee that had been studying the industry filed a report in which it urged Congress to approve the Interstate Oil Compact. Further, it proposed that a Federal agency be created to administer the interstate organization and to advise the officials of the oil-producing states. By a joint resolution the Congress of the United States approved the Interstate Oil Compact on August 27,

1935. Representatives of the signatory states conferred at Oklahoma City and organized the Interstate Oil Compact Commission, members of which were appointed to serve on four committees. These committees were to deal with conservation, consumption, co-ordination, and exports and imports. Officially, there was no suggestion that the purpose would be to stabilize prices at a profitable level. Monthly forecasts of demand, however, were issued by the United States Bureau of Mines, and the Interstate Oil Compact Commission used these to determine the state allowables.

The Interstate Oil Compact had been organized to expire in 1937, so in 1936 an effort was made to extend its life. The Federal Trade Commission, arguing that it conserved gas and assisted in unit pool operations, urged Congress to extend the compact. In Texas, Lon Smith, a member of the Railroad Commission, denounced the compact and avowed that it had served its purpose. He declared that it had served to sidetrack the movement toward Federal control, but that in his opinion neither Oklahoma nor Louisiana was abiding by the allowables fixed by the Compact Commission; therefore the organization might well be abandoned. Nevertheless, at a meeting in New Orleans in 1937 the states renewed the compact which again was approved by Congress and the President, for the purpose of conservation. Governor Marland, however, said that the governors of states could discuss prices with immunity, adding that it would be impossible to "put a state in jail." There was fear that the price of petroleum would drop again, so Marland invited the governors of the oil states to a conference at Hot Springs, Arkansas. James V. Allred, governor of Texas, refused to attend the meeting. Allred declared that the states could not do what was illegal for the oil companies, and that he would have no part in violating the antitrust laws.

The Specter of Governmental Control

Buyers suddenly slashed the prices of crude oil in August, 1939. Members of the Interstate Oil Compact Commission conferred at Oklahoma City, and quickly hurried back to their respective states. Then, state by state, the different regulatory bodies ordered oil production stopped completely for ten to fifteen days. The shutdown stopped 75 per cent of the production of the country, and affected a similar proportion of the gasoline consumed throughout the United States. No records of the meetings were produced later when members of a congressional investigating committee became inquisitive. Men who attended the meeting admitted that the "general situation" had been discussed, but they would not say that a general shutdown had been agreed upon. It appeared, however, that the commission had become a partner in the movement to restrict production for the purpose of raising prices, although control of prices was an objective that was foreign to the stated purpose of the compact. Close attention certainly had been given to market demand and production quotas, an activity that was not authorized by the compact.

In justification of the Oil Compact Commission it may be said that it has formed the chief common approach to the conservation of oil and gas since the collapse of the National Industrial Recovery Act. It has been a clearinghouse for ideas, which in itself has tended to develop a better understanding of the involved problems of the industry. On the other hand, all the oil-producing states were not members of the compact, nor did it foster uniform laws in the different commonwealths. The Compact Commission did not succeed in conducting a sustained program of research, and may be looked on as a superstructure beneath which the states generally have continued to conduct their programs of proration.

Regarding proration, heated arguments developed two

diametrically opposed beliefs. The practice of limiting production has been praised for increasing the national reserve of petroleum and for developing scientific and engineering efficiency. It has been credited with maintaining a "living price" for oil. At the same time others have denounced it as responsible for perpetuating expensive production methods and for hindering improvements in technology. Proration has been decried for stimulating drilling and the consequent elimination of independent producers, refiners, and marketers. Some opponents said that it encouraged the production of "hot oil," the operations of promoters, and countless inequalities, inequities, and dissensions within the industry. It has been blamed for the freezing of immense amounts of capital in leases, equipment, and wells—money which consequently yields only small returns to investors.

Proration was assailed by its enemies as a scheme of the major firms to limit the amount of oil that could escape from their pipe lines to the refineries of the minor concerns. It was asserted that the cost of production had little effect on the supply, demand, or price, but that the sales of petroleum were certain to go to those companies with the highest allotted production. An Oklahoma jurist declared proration to be the child of monopoly and arbitrary power. An executive of one of the large companies declared that the oil industry was not interested in preserving a supply of petroleum for future generations. Some men argued, on the contrary, that oil and gas were irreplaceable and that overproduction resulted in waste. Economic waste, it was added, resulted when rapid production caused the price of oil to fall. Laws were passed recognizing economic waste. Proration laws were even assailed when they did not prohibit declining prices. The tariff that tended to limit the importation of foreign oil was looked upon as a part of a general program to control the output of domestic wells. Although the argument on the numerous aspects of proration was violent, most men agreed that it was impossible to control production without regulation of drilling.

Closely akin to the complex question of proration was the unit plan of pool development and operation suggested in 1926 by Henry L. Doherty, who said the idea had first occurred to him in 1895. The plan called for the pooling of all the holdings of a district in the hands of one company, which was authorized to conduct all operations. The owners of the pool would share in the profits according to the ratio of their holdings. Doherty declared that the unit plan had two important virtues. It would assist in the conservation of the petroleum by eliminating many wastes, and it would aid in stabilizing the industry by resulting in more orderly and better controlled production.

Opponents of the plan at once asserted that it might cause stagnation by putting an end to competition. They believed it would tend to develop a monopoly and would amount to an illegal combination in restraint of trade. Finally, they argued, the royalty owners might not benefit from the unit operation, since the oil would be drained away through a smaller number of wells.

All arguments to the contrary, the unit plan of pool development and operation contained economic aspects that appealed to the industry. By 1930 there were eighty cases of unit operation in progress in the four states of Kansas, Texas, Oklahoma, and Louisiana. Royalty owners remained the chief opponents of the unit plan, for each wanted a well on his particular property. By 1940 four states, Arkansas, Louisiana, New Mexico, and Oklahoma, had enacted laws which permitted their regulatory bodies to force the pooling of small plots of land so as to prevent excessive drilling.

A definite effort to establish Federal control of the oil

industry was attempted in 1939 when Representative William P. Cole, Jr., chairman of a committee that had been investigating since 1934, introduced in Congress a measure that would have made the United States the supervisor of all divisions of the petroleum business. The bill proposed to establish an officer whose multitudinous duties would include investigations, demonstrations, and economic and chemical studies. The commissioner was to be assisted by a council of eighteen, including state officials, oil men, and teachers of technical subjects dealing with petroleum. At once a heated argument flourished between the supporters and opponents of the Cole Bill.

The proponents of the measure denounced state-controlled proration as the cause of excess drilling and the consequent high cost of production. This method of proration prevented the use of the most economical methods, and often in its operation it was based on the rule of capture. They contended that state proration had been responsible for the development of competition between the commonwealths. The states were accused of having done a poor job of conserving the natural resource, and the industry was assailed as having been unable to govern itself. The civil and military needs of the United States required that the waste of petroleum be stopped. It was asserted that the waste interfered with interstate commerce and that competition had become most unfair.

The opponents of the Cole Bill declared that it intended to establish an official with despotic powers. It was declared vague and indefinite. Elected state officials were avowed to be more responsive to the public good than an appointive Federal commissioner could be expected to be. The spirit of co-operation among the states was praised. Finally, the enemies of the bill asserted that it was possible for the states to permit the industry to manage itself, thereby assuring a good job. These arguments were successful in preventing the enactment of the Cole Bill.

Thus the specter of governmental control has been successfully driven off, so far; but it still remains to haunt the petroleum industry of the United States. It hovered especially near during the flush production of great oil pools, became an important factor during the First World War, and arose again in the dreary days of the depression of the thirties. Each successive movement toward governmental control appeared to be nearer success than the previous one. Some fear that the "total" Second World War may make the oil industry virtually a division of the Federal government.

Thus Tales Are Made

FICTION writers have long used the oil industry as a backdrop for their tales, often with plots hinging on the dramatic or unexpectedly sudden acquisition of wealth. Many stories have been written on the criminal activities of outlaws in the oil fields. Detective stories have been placed in boom oil towns of the Southwest. Actually the fiction writers, except in a few rare cases, have hardly done justice to the extraordinary possibilities of the field. Some of the most interesting and intriguing incidents were of little actual significance, others have become legendary. Much of the material in this chapter cannot be regarded as historically accurate, as in some cases absolute verification would be impossible.

Certainly one oil-field story has become a legend. It may have occurred once, but the regularity with which it is retold throughout the Southwest casts doubt on its authenticity. Doubtless all the significant oil pools and many of the lesser ones, from Kansas to Mexico, and Louisiana to New Mexico, have served as the scene for this bit of lore. Thousands of persons in the Southwest tell it with sincere belief in its accuracy. Here it is retold once more.

It was almost sunset as a tired teamster urged his plodding horses on, less than a mile from their destination. The terminus was a large new stake, where some men with a queer idea were planning to drill a well which they said was sure to find oil. The heavy load of rig timbers twisted as one of the great horses hesitated before plunging into a puddle of mud with the weighty burden. The teamster went into action with his whip, as two of the wheels sank into the soft soil and the wagon stopped behind the lunging horses. The great team was unable to move the loaded wagon. The driver had a great deal of sympathy for his horses; they had pulled the load nearly twenty miles since sunrise.

Grumbling and muttering, the teamster dropped from his seat to the ground and glanced at the sinking sun. To free the wagon he must unload it. Then he must drive the empty vehicle to firm ground and reload. Only a short distance remained to be driven before the lumber would be deposited near the stake, where the tired man and his plodding team would turn back. Thoughtfully the teamster gritted his teeth and stacked the heavy timbers on the ground. The team easily took the empty wagon from the mud. The man then took a short-handled ax from his tool box and sharpened a large stake, which he drove firmly into the earth near the stack of heavy lumber. They wanted a stake, so he gave them a stake.

The next day the rig-builders came and erected a derrick around the teamster's stake. The rig-builders were followed by the drilling crew, who set up their machinery and had gone deep into the earth before the owners of the well discovered the change in location. The well was completed. It opened a great new pool. Then several months passed before a well at the original location proved to be an expensive dry hole.

That story has been told with many variations. Sometimes the teamster lost his directions, or the truck broke down, or the location could not be found, or the dark eye-socket of a bleached cow's skull attracted attention, but the conclusion is always the same: the new well was a good one and the old location was dry.

For narrow escapes, there is the case of a young man who entered the oil business at Spindletop as a fireman for a drilling crew. The boilers were heated and the steam power generated by burning natural gas, with which the young man was unfamiliar. The fire was extinguished one night by turning off the gas. The next morning the young fireman turned on the gas, then crawled into the firebox to light the jets with a match. The explosion blew him from the boiler. He was not injured, but he quit the oil industry at once.

Few examples show the speculative values given to land better than that of Red Fork, in the Indian Territory. Here it was, in the summer of 1901, that an auction was held where neither seller nor buyer owned the land that was changing hands. During the excitement surrounding the Heydrick-Wick well, when adventurous men from all parts of the United States were arriving in large numbers, a man from Iowa announced that he was a surveyor. He busily platted a town near the spitting little well. Although the allotment of the Indian lands was in progress, the land still belonged to the entire Creek Nation. The enterprising surveyor was not deterred by such a slight detail as communal ownership of the land. When he had completed his plat, an auction of the lots of the proposed town was held. The sale was conducted near the oil well, and after each head-flow through the casing the bidding became brisker. One man purchased a lot and sold it within a couple of hours at a profit of several hundred dollars.

When the Indian and Oklahoma territories were merged in 1907 to form the state of Oklahoma, not all of the members of the Five Civilized Tribes had been allotted land in severalty. Among the Creeks there was a group, followers of Chitto Harjo (who was known as Crazy Snake), who resisted all efforts of the Federal officers to allot land to them. Some drunken cowboys were killed when they fired into the home of Crazy Snake while he was conferring with several of his friends. Public feeling quickly became feverish. Martial law was declared and the Oklahoma militia was sent to the scene. Federal officials felt that Crazy Snake would not receive a fair trial if arrested. He was told to hide until the excitement had passed. The Indian leader died while still in hiding, but the incident became known in local history as the Crazy Snake War, the last Indian uprising. It was neither a war nor an uprising, but Crazy Snake's followers remained adamant regarding allotment. Finally the Indian Department assigned each of them land in the stony clay hills of the western side of the Creek Nation. Hundreds of arbitrary Creek allotments were made here. Many of them were among the most valuable areas of the Cushing Pool, and one allotment of 160 acres produced a total of more than twenty-four million dollars worth of petroleum.

In hundreds of cases the unanticipated riches of an oil strike brought humorous reactions from the landowners. John McClesky was sixty-three years old in 1918 when the oil well on his farm opened the famous Ranger Pool. He had been a hard-working farmer, with a more hard-working wife. The well probably brought him an income of more than two hundred dollars a day. When he asked Mrs. McClesky what she would like, she said, "I sure do need a new ax to hack the kindlin'." A similar incident occurred when one of the big wells of East Texas was completed as a gusher. The farmer was plowing, and an excited newspaper reporter rushed up to learn how the lucky man intended to spend his wealth, only to hear that "Maw's been wantin' a new cook stove a long time."

Not everyone, however, welcomed the finding of oil.

While the streets of Wichita Falls were crowded with elbowing persons and long queues formed before the windows of the bank tellers, a rancher stood in line with a check for thirty-seven thousand dollars to deposit. It was a royalty payment from an oil company. An acquaintance asked him if he were not pleased with the money he was receiving from the oil industry. "Worst thing ever happened to the country," avowed the ranchman. "Why, they tear down the fences, pollute the water, ruin the grass, and ——— ——— ———!"

Money received from oil was variously spent and hoarded. One of the most impressive one-night spending sprees on record took place in Wichita County, Texas, in 1919, when a farmer received a certified check for fifty thousand dollars one evening. All the money was gone the next morning when the farmer watched the construction of derricks in his wheat field. Near Orange, Texas, a few years later, one of the largest oil wells in the state was completed on a truck farm. Unlike his fellow Texan, the truck farmer continued to peddle his peas and onions from door to door in Orange. Another thrifty soul was the newspaper editor in the southern part of the state who lived on a six-acre fruit farm while he worked in the near-by city. A well in the orchard struck oil, but the newspaperman continued to write headlines because "oil wells sometimes go dry." A country doctor in East Texas attended a poor and aged farm woman in her final illness. She had no money with which to pay for the medical attention, but when she died her will gave the mineral rights of the farm to the doctor. At that time there was little reason to think of oil, but later the doctor sold his mineral rights for fifty-two thousand dollars. One of the farmers near Desdemona strategically avoided the contagion of quick spending that affected most of the persons in that area during the boom. He sold his farm for $250,000 and then took a job with one of the drilling crews of the district at $5.00 a day. He explained that he could live on his wages and save the principal.

Another Desdemona farmer reacted quite differently to the prospect of money from petroleum. He had gained little more than subsistence from his agriculture, possibly because of his fondness for hunting. He owned thirteen hounds, and was distressed by their generally underfed condition. Wealth from oil aroused two pictures in his mind: thirteen well-fed hounds and a red automobile. He generously agreed to take the neighbors riding—if there was room after the dogs got in.

That wealth could bring its problems is shown by the story of a woman at Wichita Falls. Although thousands of dollars in American currency were common enough sights during the days of the Burkburnett boom, the police were astonished when a woman appeared with a suitcase filled with paper money of the state of Chihuahua, Mexico. She wanted the help of the police. She explained that her husband was the president of an oil company and that she was the vice president. She also owned some stock in several other companies, and one of her prized possessions was a sealskin coat. She and her husband had done a bit of trading, and he had swapped her some stock in their own oil company for her stock in the other companies. Then he had traded some more stock and the bag of Mexican money for her sealskin coat. He had left on business, but she had become suspicious when he did not return promptly. Now, she told the officers, she had found her coat pawned for two hundred dollars. All she had was the bag of Mexican money.

Even more astonished than those policemen was a swearing teamster at Ranger, when, during an especially muddy spell, he blocked one of the tortuous roads with his team and heavy load. The situation was complicated by the appearance of an automobile in the ruts ahead. The teamster cursed and instructed the driver of the car, a small man, to get that thing out of the way.

"Who are you, anyhow?"

"Who are you?" asked the small man in reply.

"It don't matter who I am, I work for the biggest ———— ———— ————— ————— oil company in the United States, so get the hell out of the way!"

"When you get back to town you call for your pay," quietly ordered the man in the car. "I own that company!"

Such dramatic episodes were more numerous than the many short romances and quick marriages that accompanied the expansion of the oil industry. Homely women and ignorant, ill-kept men became desirable spouses as soon as the discovery of oil brought them large incomes. The most notorious case was that of Jackson Barnett, a Creek Indian who scarcely spoke English and who was happiest with a couple of ponies at hand and a few dimes jingling in his pocket. The drilling of great oil wells on his arbitrary allotment (in the Cushing Field), which he never had seen, meant little to Jackson Barnett except that there were always dimes jingling in his pocket. The fortune of Jackson Barnett was highly significant, however, to Mrs. Anna Laura Lowe. She proposed to marry the Indian. He, eighty years old and an incompetent millionaire with a guardian, was willing to marry her. She had taken him to his first motion picture and promised a more colorful life. A fast automobile took them to Coffeyville, Kansas, where they were married before breakfast. It was suggested that the laws of Kansas might not sanction the marriage of an incompetent, so they continued to Missouri, where the regulations were not so puritanical. The matronly bride and her carefree husband returned to the modest bungalow that Barnett's guardian had built for the Indian in the blackjack oaks near Henryetta, Oklahoma. The guardian, sensing a possible legal tangle, withdrew from Barnett's affairs.

Mr. and Mrs. Barnett soon left Oklahoma for Los Angeles, where the transformation of the follower of Crazy Snake took place. Probably no man was ever more completely changed in appearance, from uncouthness to elegance, than was Jackson Barnett under the guidance of Anna Laura Lowe Barnett. His marriage and legal affairs occupied a great deal of newspaper space throughout the United States, as the oil from his 160-acre allotment made him the world's richest Indian. A settlement of the estate was arranged while he was alive, but when he died, at the age of ninety-two, there were 861 claimants to shares in the property. As Barnett never had been married until Anna Laura Lowe entered his life, direct heirs were impossible to find definitely. For years the case was in the courts, the widow receiving almost nothing from the estate, which was dissipated by litigation.

Many years after the Barnett elopement, an old Osage, also an incompetent Indian and a ward of the Federal government, took part in a similar event. He was the owner of a headright (undivided tribal interest), the estate of which was held in trust by the United States Indian Department, an allowance of thirty dollars a week being paid to him. A white woman and her family expected to gain control of the Osage's fortune through the marriage, which took place in Arkansas. The Osage agent at Pawhuska, however, refused to give the Indian even an increase in his allowance because of his marriage.

Kidnapping was not always concluded with a matrimonial service. One Billy Carolina, a descendant of a Negro freedman of the Creek tribe, had no allotment, although he was entitled to one. In the heart of the Glenn Pool was the allotment of a deceased Indian, available for reassignment because of its owner's death. A group of oil men selected Billy Carolina as the new allottee, and filled out the papers for him. While the legal and governmental arrangements were being completed, he was held in friendly custody. A group of rival oil men learned what was happening, so they spirited the Negro away from his original sponsors. Then the two groups negotiated and divided Carolina's allotment, leaving the Negro a small portion.

The oil-producing section of Oklahoma contained a strange society that included white men, Negroes, and Indians of various intermixtures. Possibly the most shrewd and capable traders were the mixed-blood Indians, who understood the Anglo-American culture and laws and at the same time kept the confidence of the tribesmen. Several of them gained wealth, prestige, and high offices through astute and none too honorable manipulations. Among the Negroes there were some with unusual ability to be disreputable. One Negro sold an allotment—which he had never received—a grand total of sixteen times, at least once while serving a sentence in prison for the same offense. In another case a Negro came to Tulsa and submitted an abstract showing a good and salable title to a tract of land. He sold a lease to an oil company for a large cash sum. He represented himself as the owner, signed the lease, got the money, and departed. This even fooled a good lawyer. The real owner of the property later sold his lease for an even higher sum.

Soon after the allotment of land in severalty to the Creek Indians had been completed, plans were made to cheat the Negro recipients of their land. A real estate company of Chicago rented an entire floor of a Muskogee office building. A large stock of watermelons, sandwiches, and liquid refreshments was purchased. Plans were made to entertain hundreds of persons all night behind locked doors. It was the intention of the company to induce the Negro allottees to sign deeds to their lands during the festivities. Only a small number of allottees attended, however, and only two deeds were signed.

There were innumerable cases of thievery under the guise of legality in the early years of Oklahoma when guardians gained control of the wealth of the allottees in the former Indian Territory. In 1908 the county courts of Oklahoma were placed in charge of the estates of the illiterate, helpless Indians, on much of whose land petroleum had been or was to be found. The law permitted the county judges to appoint guardians for the incompetent Indians. There were several cases in which the guardians were members of the families of the judges, or where the patronage might have been gained by "lending" money to the magistrates. Once in charge of a large estate, the guardian supervised all the expenditures of his ward. He could pay himself a 100 per cent commission on his ward's grocery and clothing bills. He might purchase an office building for his ward and give himself an enormous commission for services. Every personal expenditure was made through the guardian, who received a fee. On one occasion the guardian even collected something after death: the ward was buried in a pine box and a fee for an elaborate funeral was collected. Enormous sums were squandered by the Indians under the guidance of their guardians.

While many of the guardians were dishonest and without scruples regarding their obligations, some of them conscientiously took care of the estates of their wards, even accumulating more property. And though some of the judges were as disreputable as the guardians whom they appointed, there were others who were honest and able magistrates. It should be borne in mind also, in justice to the county judge, that it would have been a physical impossibility for any one judge to study even a small part of the estate matters filed in his court. The legal robbery that was taking place was not entirely a matter of negligence or irresponsibility. The fortunes of the Indians were shifted rapidly from the tribesmen, who were even stripped of their allotments. Companies sprang up that dealt only in farm land, which was acquired from the allottees at a mere fraction of its value. One man acquired land in every township of Creek County, one of the large Oklahoma counties. Another man gradually bought land from the Indians until he was believed to be the largest individual landowner in the world. The Indians traditionally had little understanding of private landholding, for under their tribal organization the soil had been communal property. By the close of the second decade of this century, the oil industry had moved farther west, thus making the remaining property of the Indians less desirable.

While many lost their property, there developed a feeling on the part of some Indians that the federal government was obliged to support them.

During the heyday of the oil industry in Osage County, many apparently honorable businessmen yielded to the temptation to steal from the Indians. The Osages received their money at the Pawhuska agency in quarterly payments, so the common practice was to collect all debts from the Indians on payment days. The Indians at best were none too careful in their business dealings, so it was not uncommon for a debt to be paid several times on as many payment days. One Osage on settling an obligation with a merchant demanded a receipt. The merchant became indignant, asserting that he never gave receipts, that he never collected a bill more than once, and that his reputation was beyond suspicion. The Indian was unimpressed and reasserted his demand with a conclusion to this effect: "Maybe what you say is true. But you give me a receipt. You might die, and I don't want to go to hell after this receipt."

In the summer of 1922, when the Osages were receiving large quarterly payments, a chautauqua visited one of the small towns of their county. Three of the Indians purchased all the performances and conducted the show free for the public.

Among the many strange characters recurrently seen in the early days of the oil industry was the "man with the doodlebug." He was always mysteriously marked from the crowd, generally by the uncommon nature of his garments. In a throng of booted men in overalls, one dressed in kid shoes, a frock coat, and a clean derby attracted attention. This man, who spoke softly, carried a shiny black box under his arm. His services were for sale, and when employed he prowled about the countryside muttering strange words and syllables until the magical black box, his doodlebug, stopped him. There, he told his employer, was the exact spot on which to drill for oil. A simpler form of the doodlebug was the forked stick, which allegedly signified the presence of oil by a downward pull when carried under tension over the "oil stream." This was the old water witch idea. In one case a farmer owned land that a large oil company wanted to lease, but he refused to sign a contract until the firm had agreed to make the first hole at the spot selected by an "oil smeller," a term now used by oil men for all such media. The well that was drilled produced about five hundred barrels of petroleum daily. The strange thing about that well was that surrounding holes in every direction were dry, which of course confirmed the farmer's faith in legerdemain.

Another odd belief of the pioneer oil men was that petroleum generally would be found in the earth near or beneath graveyards. Many wells were drilled near burial grounds, and a surprising number of them in the Southwest found petroleum. Thus the theory was strengthened by practical experience. Not until the geologists became an important factor in the industry was a satisfactory explanation offered. Hilltops were often selected for burial grounds because of the existing natural drainage. Subsurface anticlines or domes in some instances were reflected on the surface in the form of hills. Anticlines formed traps which impounded and collected petroleum. Thus, coincidentally, graveyards became associated with oil pools. It was not possible to lease all cemeteries, even for high prices, and in spite of the apparent certainty in some oil fields that oil would be obtained beneath them. During the boom in the Ranger area, one hundred thousand dollars was offered for the Merriman burial ground, not far from the city. The offer was refused, and the event became a subject for a local poet, Will Ferrell, then working at Ranger.

> All of Oildom knows the answer,
>   When the Chairman shook his head,
> Pointing past the men of millions
>   To the City of the Dead,
> "Why disturb the weary tenants
>   In yon narrow strip of sod?
> 'Tis not ours, but theirs the title,
>   Vested by the will of God.
> We, the board, have talked it over
>   Pro and con without avail,
> We reject your hundred thousand—
>   Merriman is not for sale."

A similar refusal was given by members of a church near Tonkawa.

Theories of oil accumulation were the natural accompaniment of an industry in which chance was such an important factor as it was in the early days of the southwestern oil business. Some of the theories were based entirely on ignorance and fallacious guessing, but others had more logical and thoughtful foundations. One of the most amazing theories was propounded in 1916 by a Kansas oil man after a fourteen-day trip that took him from Topeka to Beaumont and back home. North of the Kansas oil pools there was a great quantity of coal, in an area from which the terrain gradually sloped to the Gulf of Mexico. On those two facts was based the theory that the Mid-Continent oil by some queer chemical process originated in the Kansas coal fields. By gravity the fluid supposedly moved south toward the Gulf of Mexico, forming a subterranean drainage system similar to that of a river and its tributaries. It was not explained where or how, if at all, the great river of petroleum emptied at its mouth. That Kansas oil man wanted to drill a well straight into his theoretical river of petroleum.

Byron Shelley, of Tulsa, whose name should have made him a poet, offered a prize of five dollars in 1915 for the best verses on the oil fields by a native of Oklahoma. Several subjects were suggested by persons who smiled at the idea. The ruddy water of the sinuous Arkansas River was suggested as a topic. Other proposals included the chugging of the common carrier pipe lines, the tragic crack of the robber's gun, the mournful moan of the weary walking beam, and the scenic beauty of the oil-splashed landscape. In the desolate greasewood of Crane County, Texas, an uneducated driller became thoughtful as he worked through the night. With some effort he produced the following:

"I'm a driller, but I have the soul of an artist. Damn it, that field (at night) of waving flares might be part of the fire of hell, and the hissing, the despair of the souls that are being consumed. But paint, man? I can hardly write my name."

215

Casing Off*

T HE six states of the Gulf-Southwest produced 63.33 per cent of the petroleum output of the United States in 1940, a year in which more than 230 new pools were discovered by exploratory operations. It was estimated at the close of the year that the region contained 14,541,331,-000 barrels of proved and recoverable reserves, or 76.4 per cent of the known future supply of the nation. In the six states, 177,200 wells were producing oil. Of those wells in Louisiana, Texas, and Oklahoma, 497 were more than ten thousand feet deep. Twenty-six of the country's forty-six most copious oil pools had been found in the Gulf-Southwest. The cumulative yield of the southwestern states alone by 1941 had reached 14,347,858,000 barrels, while the entire world outside the United States had produced only 13,381,523,000 barrels. Of the 309 major pools discovered in eighty years in the United States, 235 had been found in this region in the last fifty years. The cumulative output of the whole country, including the six southwestern states, was 23,805,051,000 barrels. Thus the Gulf-Southwest had become much the most important producing region of the world.

With every nation on the globe using lubricants from the United States, the world's chief refining district had

*In the parlance of the oil industry, "casing off" refers to the operations that surround the closing of a formation.

developed in Texas, which state accounted for almost one-third of the nation's processing capacity. Nearly one-fourth of the country's refining capacity was concentrated on the Gulf Coast of Texas. One-tenth of the national processing was done in the Beaumont–Port Arthur area alone, where the plants were supplied with crude oil by twenty pipe lines. Much of the southwestern oil, nevertheless, was refined by plants on the Atlantic Coast, having been moved there by rail, tank ship, or pipe line. One pipe line, moving Kansas and Oklahoma petroleum, has for years taken a continuous stream of oil across the intervening states, under the Hudson River, through Central Park, and to the stills of a refinery on Long Island. Improved methods of refining, one purportedly yielding 80 per cent of high-grade gasoline from the poorest crude, were expected to decrease the waste of processing. Products valued at nearly $2,500,000,000 were yielded by the refineries of the United States in 1939.

By 1940 the petroleum industry of the United States was dominated by about twenty-five integrated companies with international or world-wide holdings. There were hundreds of small companies, of course, which would remain in the industry as long as the stripper wells continued to produce. The total production of the small companies was larger than ever before, although their percentage of the aggregate output was lower than it had been previously. It was not likely that these minor concerns would take a leading part in the future explorations, because the anticipated deeper production would require large capital investments. Drilling costs in 1940 varied from two thousand dollars in shallow Texas pools to considerably more than one hundred thousand dollars in the hard formations of northern Louisiana. Most of the shallow pools were believed to have been discovered, which suggested more costly, deeper wells in the future. The cost of prospecting, all of

Flush Production

the United States considered, amounted to about thirteen cents for each barrel of oil discovered and produced. The average cost of the wells was $21,600, and about one hole in three was dry. All divisions considered, the oil industry had become the third largest in the United States, representing an estimated investment of twelve to fifteen billion dollars.

Directly and indirectly, the oil industry in the states of the Southwest had become the most important source of governmental revenue. There were a large number of taxes, including: general property tax, production tax, gasoline tax, sales tax, corporate income tax, automobile license, chauffeur's registration, motor operator's fee, occupation tax, chain store tax, pipe-line regulation tax, tax on the manufacture of carbon black, motor vehicle mileage tax, county tax, municipal tax, school district tax, inspection fee, kerosene tax, natural gas tax, and lubricating oil tax.

THE THIRTY HUGE POOLS OF THE GULF-SOUTHWEST[a]

Pool	State	County	Year Found	Barrels, 1940	All Years, Cumulative
BILLION OR MORE BARRELS:					
East Texas	Texas	5 counties[b]	1930	140,851,200	1,588,672,984
Seminole Area[c]	Okla.	4 counties[d]	1926	38,882,074	1,114,629,142
HALF-BILLION BARRELS:					
Oklahoma City	Okla.	Oklahoma	1928	35,806,489	514,566,482
300–400 MILLION BARRELS:					
Smackover	Arkansas	Ouachita & Union	1922	5,518,006	383,648,090
Cushing	Okla.	Creek	1912	3,305,713	356,124,810
200–300 MILLION BARRELS:					
Yates	Texas	Pecos	1926	6,869,370	254,195,989
Glenn	Okla.	Creek	1905	1,241,142	219,270,877
Burbank	Okla.	Osage & Kay	1920	2,850,210	201,876,928

Casing Off

100–200 MILLION
BARRELS:

Hendrick	Texas	Winkler	1926	2,934,991	198,918,836
Healdton	Okla.	Carter	1913	3,177,702	187,466,587
Eldorado	Kansas	Butler	1917	2,648,939	174,618,269
Caddo	Louisiana	Caddo	1904	3,020,000	159,540,420
Burkburnett	Texas	Wichita	1912	e	152,315,960
St. Louis	Okla.	Pottawatomie	1927	9,497,446	148,020,661
Electra	Texas	Wichita	1911	e	136,669,409
Seminole City	Okla.	Seminole	1926	2,502,947	126,605,191
Spindletop	Texas	Jefferson	1901	611,086	126,128,691
Humble	Texas	Harris	1904	966,099	125,854,777
Van	Texas	Van Zandt	1929	4,460,165	125,627,486
Earlsboro	Okla.	Seminole	1926	1,500,576	124,120,985
Tonkawa	Okla.	Kay	1921	623,715	120,733,142
Rodessa (total)	3 states	4 counties	1930	14,171,321	117,218,985
Rodessa	Louisiana	Caddo	1930	6,910,000	67,968,920
Rodessa	Texas	Cass & Marion	1935	6,554,164	43,518,991
Rodessa	Arkansas	Miller	1937	707,157	5,731,074
Bowlegs	Okla.	Seminole	1926	2,468,591	116,786,040
Conroe	Texas	Montague	1931	9,251,461	116,782,296
Powell	Texas	Navarro	1901	633,572	114,710,698
Little River	Okla.	Seminole	1927	2,414,979	109,475,881

NEARLY 100 MILLION
BARRELS:

Mexia	Texas	Limestone	1921	570,732	97,297,635
Big Lake	Texas	Regan	1923	2,147,640	96,743,874
Chalk	Texas	Howard & Glasscock	1926	4,946,330	94,512,397
Hobbs	N. M.	Lea	1929	3,786,631	94,482,122

GRAND TOTAL   7,614,834,629

a This table was taken from a compilation published in *The Oil Weekly,* Vol. C, No. 8 (January 27, 1941), 76.

b Rusk, Gregg, Smith, Upshur, Cherokee.

c Includes more than thirty pools, five of which are also listed individually: St. Louis, Seminole City, Earlsboro, Bowlegs, Little River.

d Hughes, Pottawatomie, Okfuskee, Seminole.

e Data for 1940 not available. Production about the same as in 1939, but not included in this table.

Three taxes alone yielded thirty million dollars for the state government of Oklahoma in 1939. The taxes accounted for 40 per cent of the retail price of gasoline. In the six states of this study, gasoline taxes amounted to $101,741,000 in 1939, and in the same year $40,454,211 was collected in severance taxes.

Flush Production

Much has been written about the unwise extravagance of persons who received wealth from the petroleum industry, but little has been said about the sound and constructive use to which many put their money. Hundreds of farmers moved to college towns and educated their children, afterwards establishing them in business or on good farms. Some invested their royalties and bonuses in agricultural improvements, better barns, fences, windmills, convenient homes, and telephones. Cooking and heating, almost without exception, were done with natural gas.

Benefits of the oil industry were extended to many thousands of persons through gifts to public institutions. At Sand Springs, Oklahoma, an orphanage and a widows' colony were established and maintained as the private charity of one oil man. A historical collection at the University of Oklahoma was financed by an oil fortune. Magnificent churches have been erected throughout the Southwest by individuals whose wealth came from the petroleum business. Colleges, universities, art galleries, and hospitals of the region have been the beneficiaries of large endowments from oil wealth.

Just as the industry has played an important part in the social and economic life of the nation, it has likewise been a powerful influence in the political life of the oil-producing states. The campaign platforms of candidates for state and national offices have deferred to the industry. Truly the petroleum industry of the Southwest is of far more than regional importance. It is internationally significant, a fact that is even more true because the leading companies conduct their operations on a world-wide scale.

ABSORPTION PROCESS: The process of extracting gasoline from natural gas by passing the gas through a medium capable of absorbing the gasoline, from which it can later be recovered.

AIR LIFT: A system of producing oil by forcing air through a pipe submerged below the fluid level of the well. Because of this air the column of liquid in the casing is made lighter, and an upward flow results.

ALLOWABLE: When the maximum potential production from a well has been determined, the regulatory officers decide what amount shall be produced. This percentage is known as the allowable.

ARTESIAN WELL: A well, usually quite deep, in which the pressure is so great that it forces the liquid to the surface, making pumping unnecessary.

ASPHALT BASE: Petroleum that yields asphalt but little or no paraffin.

BLANKET LEASE: This term is applied to a contract that covers a large area. For example, the entire Osage Reservation was leased to one company before the land was allotted to the Indians in severalty.

BLOWOUT: A violent escape of gas and/or oil causing the crew to lose control of the well.

CABLE SYSTEM, CABLE TOOLS: The drilling that is performed with tools suspended from a flexible cable, which alternately lifts and drops. The bit at the end of the cable does the drilling. This method of drilling was devised in ancient China, and has been called the churn drill.

Flush Production

CAPPED: When a well is completed, or nearly completed, but is not permitted to produce, it is capped, which means that the casing is closed.

CARBON BLACK: A name for "lampblack," which is the residue acquired by burning natural gas in the presence of little air.

CASING: The large pipes supporting the walls of a well, which prevent caving of the walls or the entrance of water, or both.

CASINGHEAD GASOLINE: From the wet gas that is produced from an oil well it is possible to manufacture gasoline of very high volatility. Loosely, this term has also been used to refer to gasoline with a great deal of butane and propane content.

CORE DRILL: A hollow drill designed for extracting cores from the hole to gain geological information.

FISHTAIL: The term indicates a rotary bit that is wedge-shaped, often with the two sides of the point bent in opposite directions.

FLUSH POOL or FLUSH PERIOD: These terms apply to the early period of a pool's life when the wells are yielding at capacity or are capable of high production.

GAS-OIL RATIO: The proportion of gas to oil that is produced by a specific pool or well, usually expressed in cubic feet per barrel of oil.

GUSHER: An oil well from which petroleum flows spontaneously because of the accumulation of gas under pressure in the oil-bearing formation.

HORIZON: Geologists use this word to indicate an oil- or gas-bearing zone.

INDIAN NATIONS: In the nineteenth century when the eastern Indians were moved to lands west of the Mississippi River, they were organized with their own native governments. The program amounted to the organization and establishment of little nations for the Five Civilized Tribes.

LOG: The driller's report of formations, water, oil, and gas encountered, possibly including much detail.

222

Glossary

MAGNETOMETER: A geophysical instrument used for measuring the magnetic intensity of subsurface formations.

MULTIPLE DRILLING: The practice of making several wells from one location of the drilling rig. It may be done by drilling slant holes of different depths to reach several horizons; or through the use of whipstocks the wells may be turned so as to drain only one formation at widely separated points.

OFFSETS: Since petroleum is somewhat migratory and the subsurface pressures cause it to move toward the nearest outlet, leaseholders have developed the practice of protecting their properties by drilling wells opposite the holes of their neighbors. These wells are known as offsets.

POTENTIAL: When a well is completed, it is permitted to produce for a test period and the gas or petroleum is measured so that the possible yield can be calculated. The resulting figure is the potential, or the "ability" of a well to produce.

RESERVOIR PRESSURE: This term applies to the energy in the pool which assists in the extraction of the petroleum. It may consist of a large amount of gas, or it may be derived from other factors, such as water or earth pressure.

RESTRICTED INDIANS: Restricted Indians are those who are wards of the United States Government, completely or in part. The fully restricted Indians fare better in the conservation of their oil property than do those whose restrictions are removed; many of the latter are left at the mercy of unscrupulous Anglo-Americans.

ROTARY BIT: The cutting point of the drill pipe in cases where the work is done through rotation of the bit instead of through the churning movement. Some of the rotary bits are wedge-shaped; many of them are hard cones or rollers which also revolve as the bit turns.

ROUSTABOUT: A laborer engaged in general lease work of varied detail.

STILL: Part of a refinery, where oil is heated to drive off the hydrocarbon vapors.

223

Flush Production

STRIPPER: A stripper well is one that has already yielded most of its oil, but from which a few barrels of oil and water can be pumped each day. Strippers are generally the least valuable of all oil wells, but they still produce a large portion of the grand total.

TANK FARM: An area that has been set aside for the storage of petroleum in large steel reservoirs.

TOOL-DRESSER: This word applies to the oil-field laborers whose principal task at a cable-tool drilling well is that of assisting the driller.

TORSION BALANCE: A geophysical instrument to measure the rate of change in the value of the acceleration of gravity at different points on the earth's surface.

WILDCAT: A well drilled in an area where the presence of oil or gas is uncertain.

FEDERAL AND STATE DOCUMENTS
AND PUBLICATIONS

Arkansas Board of Conservation. *Discussion of Petroleum Development in Arkansas, 1937–1938*. El Dorado, January, 1939.

Arkansas Geological Survey. *Geology of the Arkansas Paleozoic Area With Especial Reference to Oil and Gas Possibilities*. Little Rock, 1930.

Arkansas Oil and Gas Commission. *General Rules and Regulations Relating to Oil and Gas*, Orders 2–39. El Dorado, March, 1939.

Beal, Carl H. *The Decline and Ultimate Production of Oil Wells, With Notes on the Valuation of Oil Properties*, Department of the Interior, Bureau of Mines. Washington, 1919.

Bell, H. W. *The Monroe Gas Field*, Department of Conservation of Louisiana, *Bulletin No. 12*. Baton Rouge, n.d.

Blatchley, Raymond S. *Waste of Oil and Gas in the Mid-Continent Fields*, Department of the Interior, Bureau of Mines. Washington, 1913.

Day, David T. "The Petroleum Resources of the United States," United States Geological Survey, *Bulletin 394*, 30. Washington, 1909.

Department of Commerce. *Fifteenth Census of the United States, 1930, Population*, IV. Washington, 1933.

Department of Commerce, Bureau of Corporations. *Conditions in the Healdton Oil Field*, March 15, 1915. Washington, 1915.

Flush Production

Department of the Interior. *Laws, Decisions, and Regulations Affecting the Work of the Commission to the Five Civilized Tribes,* 1893–1906. Washington, 1906.

Department of the Interior, Commissioner of Indian Affairs. *Annual Reports,* 1886–1939. Washington, 1886–1939.

Department of the Interior, United States Geological Survey. *Mineral Resources of the United States,* 1875–1931. Washington, 1875–1931.

———. *Minerals Yearbook,* 1932–39. Washington, 1932–39.

Eagin, Frank O., and Eaton, C. W. (compilers). *Oklahoma Statutes,* 1931, II. Oklahoma City, 1932.

Eliot, Charles B. *Petroleum Industry of the Gulf Southwest,* Department of Commerce, Domestic Commerce Series, No. 44, Commercial Survey of the Gulf Southwest, Part II. Washington, 1931.

Ely, Northcutt (compiler). *The Oil and Gas Conservation Statutes.* Washington, 1933.

Exact Copy of Original Lease—Mining Lease, Osage Agency, Oklahoma Territory, 1896, for Prospecting and Mining for Oil and Gas upon the Osage Reservation, Oklahoma.

Federal Oil Conservation Board. *Complete Record of Public Hearings,* February 10–11, 1926. Washington, 1926.

———. *Reports* I, III, V. Washington, 1929, 1932.

Federal Trade Commission. *Report on the Price of Gasoline in 1915.* Washington, 1917.

———. *Petroleum Industry—Prices, Profits and Competition,* Senate Document No. 61, 70 Cong., 1 sess. Washington, 1928.

Ferguson, T. B. *Report of the Governor of Oklahoma,* 1904. Washington, 1904.

Fowler, H. C., and Cattell, R. A. "Influence of Petroleum Technology Upon Composite Interest in Oil," *Minerals Yearbook,* 1935, Part III, 771. Washington, 1935.

Frantz, Frank. *Report of the Governor of Oklahoma,* 1906. Washington, 1906.

Geological Survey of Louisiana. *A Report on the Underground Waters of Louisiana.* Baton Rouge, 1905.

226

Bibliography

Haworth, Erasmus. *Historical Outline of the Oil and Gas Industry in Kansas,* Kansas Geological Survey, *Bulletin No. 3.* Topeka, 1917.

Hill, H. B., and Sutton, Chase E. *Production and Development Problems in the Powell Oil Field, Navarro County, Texas,* Department of the Interior, Bureau of Mines. Washington, 1928.

House of Representatives. *House Resolution 290,* 76 Cong., 1 sess.

————. *House Resolution 7372,* 76 Cong., 1 sess.

————. *Indian Affairs in Oklahoma, House Report 1527,* 68 Cong., 2 sess.

House of Representatives, Committee on Mines and Mining. *Hearings, Amarillo Helium Plant, H. R. 10200,* 71 Cong., 2 sess. Washington, 1930.

Hutchison, L. L. "Oil and Gas," Oklahoma Geological Survey, *Bulletin No. 1,* 15. Norman, 1908.

Louisiana State University and A. and M. College. *A Preliminary Report on the Geology of Louisiana.* Baton Rouge, 1899.

Mills, Lawrence (compiler). *Oklahoma Indian Land Laws* (second edition). St. Louis, 1924.

Moore, Raymond C. *Oil and Gas Resources of Kansas,* State Geological Survey of Kansas, *Bulletin 3.* Topeka, 1917.

Neal, R. O., and Perrott, G. St. J. *Carbon Black—Its Manufacture, Properties and Uses,* Department of the Interior, Bureau of Mines, *Bulletin 192.* Washington, 1922.

Oklahoma Geological Survey. *Bulletin No. 2, Preliminary Report on the Rock Asphalt, Asphaltite, Petroleum and Natural Gas in Oklahoma.* Norman, 1911.

————. *Bulletin No. 19, Petroleum and Natural Gas in Oklahoma.* Norman, 1915.

————. *Bulletin No. 40, Oil and Gas in Oklahoma.* Norman, 1928.

Petroleum Administrative Board. *Operation of the New Pool Plans of Orderly Development Under the Code of Fair Competition for the Petroleum Industry.* Washington, 1936.

227

Flush Production

——. *Final Report of the Marketing Division,* Department of the Interior. Washington, 1936.

——. *Report on the Cost of Producing Petroleum.* Washington, 1935.

Powers, Sidney. "Petroleum Geology in Oklahoma," *Bulletin No. 40,* Oklahoma Geological Survey. Norman, 1928.

Public Law No. 14, 74 Cong., 1 sess. *Statutes at Large,* Vol. XLIX, Part I, 30. Washington, 1936.

Ross, J. S. *Engineering Report of the Cotton Valley Field, Webster Parish, La.,* Department of the Interior, Bureau of Mines. Washington, 1931.

Securities and Exchange Commission. *General Rules and Regulations, Under the Securities Act of 1933.* Washington, 1941.

——. *Sixth Annual Report, 1940.* Washington, 1941.

Smith, Carl D. *The Glenn Oil and Gas Pool and Vicinity,* United States Geological Survey, *Bulletin 541,* 34. Washington, 1913.

Statutes at Large of the United States of America, XLVIII (in 2 parts). Washington, 1934.

Subcommittee of the Committee on Finance, United States Senate. *Hearings on S. 790,* 75 Cong., 1 sess. Washington, 1937.

Subcommittee of the Committee on Interstate and Foreign Commerce, House of Representatives. *Hearing on House Resolution 290 and H. R. 7372* (in 5 parts), 76 Cong., 1 sess. Washington, 1939–40.

Supreme Court of the United States. *Opinion in the Case of Panama Refining Company et. al., and Amazon Petroleum Corporation et. al., Senate Document No. 10,* 74 Cong., 1 sess. Washington, 1935.

University Geological Survey of Kansas. *Special Report on Oil and Gas,* IX. Topeka, 1908.

Wade, Gustav. *Mechanical Equipment Used in the Drilling and Production of Oil and Gas Wells in the Oklahoma City Pool,* Department of the Interior, Bureau of Mines, *Technical Paper 561.* Washington, 1934.

Wegemann, Carroll H., and Heald, Kenneth C. "The Healdton Oil Field, Carter County, Oklahoma," United States Geological Survey, *Bulletin 621,* 13. Washington, 1916.

Bibliography

Wilson, M. E. *The Occurrence of Oil and Gas in Missouri,* Missouri Bureau of Geology and Mines. Rolla, 1922.

Winchester, Dean E. *The Oil and Gas Resources of New Mexico,* State Bureau of Mines and Mineral Resources, *Bulletin No. 9.* Socorro, 1933.

SCHOLARLY PUBLICATIONS

American Association of Petroleum Geologists. *Structure of Typical American Oil Fields,* I, II. Chicago, 1929.

Bradley, Virginia. "The Petroleum Industry of the Gulf Coast Salt Dome Area," *Economic Geography,* Vol. XV, No. 4 (October, 1939), 395.

Condra, G. E. "Opening of the Indian Territory," American Geographic Society, *Bulletin,* Vol. XXXIX, No. 6 (June, 1907), 321.

Ely, Northcutt. "The Conservation of Oil," *The Harvard Law Review,* Vol. LI, No. 7 (May, 1938), 1209.

Forbes, Gerald. "The Passing of the Small Oil Man," *The Southern Economic Journal,* Vol. VII, No. 2 (October, 1940), 204.

————. "History of the Osage Blanket Lease," *The Chronicles of Oklahoma,* Vol. XIX, No. 1 (March, 1941), 70.

————. "Oklahoma Oil and Indian Land Tenure," *Agricultural History,* Vol. XV, No. 3 (October, 1941), 189.

————. "Shaffer County: A Southwestern Boom Episode," *The Southwestern Social Science Quarterly,* Vol. XXI, No. 1 (June, 1940), 23.

Goodrich, H. B. "Early Discoveries of Petroleum in the United States," *Economic Geology,* Vol. XXVII, No. 2 (March-April, 1932), 160.

Hart, James P. "Oil, the Courts, and the Railroad Commission," *The Southwestern Historical Quarterly,* Vol. XLIV, No. 3 (January, 1941), 303.

Pogue, Joseph E. *Economics of the Petroleum Industry* (pamphlet), New York, 1939. (Advance printing of chapter of *The Elements of the Petroleum Industry,* E. DeGolyer [editor], American Institute of Mining and Metallurgical Engineers, under the Seeley W. Mudd Fund.)

Flush Production

Webb, Wilfred D. "The Interstate Oil Compact—Theory and Practice," *The Southwestern Social Science Quarterly*, Vol. XXI, No. 4 (March, 1941), 293.

Wright, Muriel H. "First Oklahoma Oil was Produced in 1859," *The Chronicles of Oklahoma*, Vol. IV, No. 4 (December, 1926), 320.

DISSERTATIONS AND THESES

Conrod, Robert L. "Production Technique and the Supply of Oil and Oil Products," doctor's dissertation, University of Texas, 1934.

———. "State Regulation of the Oil and Gas Industry in Texas," master's thesis, University of Texas, 1931.

Garner, L. J. "History of Hutchinson County," master's thesis, Southern Methodist University, 1930.

Martin, Everett Armstrong. "A History of the Spindletop Oil Pool," master's thesis, University of Texas, 1934.

Palmer, John Derwin. "A History of the Desdemona Oil Boom," master's thesis, Hardin-Simmons University, 1938.

Robinson, Gilbert L. "History of the Healdton Oil Field," master's thesis, University of Oklahoma, 1937.

Sandefer, Marguerite. "The Development of the Oil Industry in Wichita County," master's thesis, University of Texas, 1938.

Thomas, Robert Edward. "A Tariff on Oil," master's thesis, University of Texas, 1933.

Wagner, Mrs. Jimmie. "The Ranger Oil Boom," master's thesis, Southern Methodist University, 1935.

Williams, Guy Yandell. "Mineral Oils of Oklahoma and Indian Territory," bachelor's thesis, University of Oklahoma, 1906.

ARTICLES IN TRADE JOURNALS

Albright, J. C. "The Panhandle May Have Twenty Years More of Producing Life," *The Oil Weekly*, Vol. LXXIV, No. 9 (August 13, 1934), 31.

Bancroft, D. H. "Zwolle Shows Reward of Persistency," *The Oil and Gas Journal*, Vol. XXVIII, No. 37 (January 30, 1930), 57.

Bibliography

Beaty, A. L. "Petroleum's Future," *The Oil and Gas Journal*, Vol. XXI, No. 29 (December 14, 1922), 49.

Bignell, L. G. E. "East Texas Oil Field Insured of Long Life by Good Engineering," *The Oil and Gas Journal*, Vol. XXXIV, No. 5 (June 20, 1935), 11.

———. "Shallow Water Bearing Sands Provide Supply for Lea County, New Mexico," *The Oil and Gas Journal*, Vol. XXXIV, No. 26 (November 14, 1935), 36.

———. "Submergible Electric Oil Well Pump," *The Oil and Gas Journal*, Vol. XXVIII, No. 34 (January 9, 1930), 36.

———. "Deflected Drilling Would Enable State to Get Oil Under Capitol Building," *The Oil and Gas Journal*, Vol. XXXIV, No. 34 (January 9, 1936), 13.

Bowles, Charles E. "Texas—Yesterday, Today and Tomorrow," *The Independent Monthly*, Vol. II, No. 2 (May, 1931), 12.

———. "Oklahoma—Yesterday, Today and Tomorrow," *The Independent Monthly*, Vol. II, No. 3 (June, 1931), 9.

Bredberg, L. E. "Year's Record of Greatest Oil Field," *The Oil and Gas Journal*, Vol. XXX, No. 37 (January 28, 1932), 58.

———. "May Be World's Largest Oil Field," *The Oil and Gas Journal*, Vol. XXIX, No. 37 (January 29, 1931), 106.

Carter, Charles B. "Southwest Texas Has Every Type of Drilling Condition," *The Oil Weekly*, Vol. LXXIV, No. 13 (September 10, 1934), 22.

"Crude Reserves Shown by Fields," *The Oil and Gas Journal*, Vol. XXXV, No. 37 (January 28, 1937), 36.

Crumpton, J. R. "Rodessa One of Outstanding Oil Pools Discovered in 1935," *The Oil and Gas Journal*, Vol. XXXIV, No. 37 (January 30, 1936), 137.

Dameron, James H. "History Making Pipe Line Building," *The Oil and Gas Journal*, Vol. XXVII, No. 37 (January 31, 1929), 98.

———. "Three Famous Louisiana Oil Fields," *The Oil and Gas Journal*, Vol. XXV, No. 23 (October 28, 1926), 75.

Deussen, Alexander. "Tex-La Gulf Coast and Nation's Crude Oil Reserves," *The Oil Weekly*, Vol. LXXIV, No. 5 (July 16, 1934), 22.

Doherty, W. T. "The Permian Basin and Its Drilling and Production Problems," *The Oil Weekly,* Vol. LXXXIX, No. 4 (April 4, 1938), 26.

Dott, Robert H. "Kansas' Future Crude Oil Reserve Status," *The Oil Weekly,* Vol. LXXVI, No. 6 (January 21, 1935), 15; No. 8 (February 4, 1935), 19; No. 9 (February 11, 1935), 21.

―――. "Discoveries Required to Maintain Status of Production in Oklahoma," *The Oil Weekly,* Vol. LXXIII, No. 7 (April 30, 1934), 15; No. 8 (May 7, 1934), 14; No. 9, (May 14, 1934), 15.

Dwyer, J. L. "Modify Anti-Trust Laws, Says Hoover," *The Oil and Gas Journal,* Vol. XXV, No. 23 (October 28, 1926), 29.

―――. "Prairie Aided Mid-Continent Growth," *The Oil and Gas Journal,* Vol. XXV, No. 20 (October 7, 1926), 78.

Ellzey, B. V. "The Hunt for Oil in New Mexico," *The Oil Weekly,* Vol. XV, No. 3 (October 18, 1919), 178.

―――. "Frenzied Finance Goes the Limit With Boom On," *The Oil Weekly,* Vol. XV, No. 3 (October 18, 1919), 170.

Ely, Northcutt. "Legal Restraints on Drilling and Production," *The Oil Weekly,* Vol. LXXXVII, No. 12 (November 29, 1937), 28; No. 13 (December 6, 1937), 30.

Francher, George H., and Barnes, Kenneth B. "Water Flooding in the Mid-Continent," *The Oil Weekly,* Vol. LXXIX, No. 7 (October 28, 1935), 31.

Galey, Thomas M. "History of the Mid-Continent Oil Field," *The Oil and Gas Journal,* Vol. XXII, No. 21 (October 18, 1923), 56.

Gibbs, L. Vernon. "Offers Plan for Federal Cooperation," *The Oil and Gas Journal,* Vol. XXVI, No. 33 (January 5, 1928), 33.

Green, W. E. "The City Where Knocks Became Boosts," *The Oil Weekly,* Vol. XV, No. 3 (October 18, 1919), 194.

Hager, Dorsey. "Lady Luck or Law of Probabilities Played Lead Part in Discovery of Many Oil Fields," *The Oil and Gas Journal,* Vol. XXXIII, No. 33 (January 3, 1935), 50.

Bibliography

Heald, K. C. "Deep Well Drilling Problems and Their Solution," *The Oil Weekly*, Vol. LXXXI, No. 13 (June 8, 1936), 19.

"History of the Gulf Coast Development from Spindletop to Blue Ridge," *The Oil Weekly*, Vol. XV, No. 3 (October 18, 1919), 88.

"History of Twenty-Three Years Oil and Gas Development in Osage," *National Petroleum News*, Vol. V, No. 11 (August 6, 1919), 66.

Hubbard, William E. "Diminishing Allowables per Well," *The Oil Weekly*, Vol. LXXXIII, No. 7 (October 26, 1936), 36.

Ivy, John S. "The Rodessa Oil Field," *The Oil Weekly*, Vol. LXXXI, No. 5 (April 13, 1936), 21.

James, G. H. "Will Control of Oil Injure Industry?" *The Oil and Gas Journal*, Vol. XVI, No. 37 (February 14, 1918), 32.

Kates, Phillip. "Cooperation, Not Coercion, Needed," *The Oil and Gas Journal*, Vol. XXV, No. 20 (October 7, 1926), 31.

Kern, Charles E. "General Leasing Bill and Ferry Lake," *The Oil and Gas Journal*, Vol. XV, No. 39 (March 1, 1917), 30.

King, H. H. "Water Disposal Plan," *The Oil Weekly*, Vol. LXXX, No. 10 (February 17, 1936), 14.

————. "West Texas–New Mexico District Again is Booming," *The Oil Weekly*, Vol. LXXXVI, No. 6 (July 19, 1937), 32.

"Laws to Aid Industry to Govern Itself," *The Oil and Gas Journal*, Vol. XXVII, No. 33 (January 3, 1929), 30.

Lee, Marvin. "The Crude Oil Reserves of Western Kansas," *The Oil Weekly*, Vol. LXXXV, No. 8 (May 3, 1937), 48.

Leyendecker, Charles. "Gulf Coast Reserves," *The Oil Weekly*, Vol. LXXXII, No. 9 (August 10, 1936), 22.

————. "South Louisiana Reserves Enhanced During 1937," *The Oil Weekly*, Vol. LXXXVIII, No. 10 (February 14, 1938), 49.

Logan, L. J. "West Kansas Raises Production of State," *The Oil Weekly*, Vol. LXXXV, No. 8 (May 3, 1937), 53.

McIntyre, James. "Production Continues Far Above Allowable as Set by Government; Illegal Oil Persists," *The Oil and Gas Journal*, Vol. XXXII, No. 36 (January 25, 1934), 9.

————. "Tonkawa Has Produced 34,352,916 Barrels," *The Oil and Gas Journal,* Vol. XXIII, No. 21 (April 24, 1924), 58.

————. "East Texas Depressed Whole Industry," *The Oil and Gas Journal,* Vol. XXX, No. 37 (January 28, 1932), 56.

————. "Big Men of Oil Industry Convene," *The Oil and Gas Journal,* Vol. XXI, No. 28 (December 7, 1922), 62.

Mallon, Hugh D. "Cole Committee Bill to Ratify Compact and Create Federal Oil Commission," *The Oil and Gas Journal,* Vol. XXXIV, No. 10 (July 25, 1935), 22.

Mills, Brad. "Production Practices Directed Toward Prolonging Producing Life in Past Year," *The Oil Weekly,* Vol. LXXXVI, No. 2 (June 21, 1937), 16.

————. "New Drilling Trends," *The Oil Weekly,* Vol. LXXX, No. 7 (January 27, 1936), 23.

————. "Texas-Louisiana Gulf Coast, One of World's Greatest Areas Has Bright Future," *The Oil Weekly,* Vol. LXXXVI, No. 13 (September 6, 1937), 24.

————. "East Texas Field is Now Feeling Its Age," *The Oil Weekly,* Vol. LXXXVII, No. 12 (November 29, 1937), 22.

————. "The Gulf Coast as a Deep Oil Reserve," *The Oil Weekly,* Vol. LXXXIII, No. 9 (November 9, 1936), 46.

————. "Plugging Back May Make Smackover Wells Profitable," *The Oil Weekly,* Vol. LXXXVII, No. 1 (September 13, 1937), 17.

————. "Rodessa's Possibilities," *The Oil Weekly,* Vol. LXXVIII, No. 11 (August 26, 1935), 20.

————. "Drilling Practices," *The Oil Weekly,* Vol. LXXXVI, No. 1 (June 14, 1937), 50.

————. "Crude's Properties Influence its Uses," *The Oil Weekly,* Vol. LXXXIII, No. 2 (September 21, 1936), 18.

————. "Methods of Controlling Pressures," *The Oil Weekly,* Vol. LXXXVI, No. 1 (June 14, 1937), 85.

————. "Economic Aspects of Deep Drilling are Far Reaching," *The Oil Weekly,* Vol. LXXXV, No. 5 (April 12, 1937), 20.

————. "Spindletop Contributed Much in Equipment to Early Engineering," *The Oil Weekly,* Vol. LXXVI, No. 3 (December 31, 1934), 30.

Bibliography

Morris, W. S. "General Conditions in the East Texas Field," *The Oil Weekly*, Vol. LXXXV, No. 12 (May 31, 1937), 35.

"National Committee to Study Situation," *The Oil and Gas Journal*, Vol. XXVII, No. 34 (January 10, 1929), 29.

Nye, George L., and Miller, E. B., Jr. "The Present and Future of Pumping in the East Texas Field," *The Oil Weekly*, Vol. LXXXV, No. 12 (May 31, 1937), 24.

Parker, R. D. "The Colossal Waste of Natural Gas in the Panhandle of Texas," *The Oil Weekly*, Vol. LXXVI, No. 4 (January 7, 1935), 35.

Pitzer, P. W., and West, C. K. "Acid Treatment of Lime Wells Explained and Methods Described," reprinted from *The Oil and Gas Journal*, Vol. XXXIII, No. 27 (November 22, 1934).

Post, Earl S. "Multiple Wells," *The Oil Weekly*, Vol. LXXXVIII, No. 6 (January 17, 1938), 50.

―――. "Coring Increased and Improved Past Year," *The Oil Weekly*, Vol. LXXXVI, No. 1 (June 14, 1937), 64.

―――. "South Texas Reserves," *The Oil Weekly*, Vol. LXXIX, No. 11 (November 25, 1935), 21.

Powers, Bryant. "From Beaver Switch to Burkburnett," *The Oil Weekly*, Vol. XV, No. 4 (October 25, 1919), 55.

Pratt, Wallace E. "Future of Oil in America as Viewed in Light of Present Developments," *The Oil and Gas Journal*, Vol. XXXIV, No. 16 (September 5, 1935), 24.

Pyre, R. B. "Motion for New Trial is Filed Following Verdict at Madison," *The Oil and Gas Journal*, Vol. XXXVI, No. 37 (January 27, 1938), 57.

Rosaire, E. E. "Exploration by the Reflection Seismograph," *The Oil Weekly*, Vol. LXXXVI, No. 1 (June 14, 1937), 70.

Rowley, Andrew M. "Texas Gas Law Forcing Readjustment in Operation of Three Big Industries," *The Oil and Gas Journal*, Vol. XXXIV, No. 11 (August 1, 1935), 12.

Salnikov, I. S., and Haider, M. L. "Pressure Maintenance and Unitization, South Burbank Pool," *The Oil Weekly*, Vol. LXXXV, No. 13 (June 7, 1937), 34.

Sclater, K. C. "A 7,000-Foot Relief Well Hits its Mark," *The Petroleum Engineer*, Vol. VIII, No. 2 (November, 1926), 28.

Shaw, S. F. "Advantage of Large Casing in Gas-Lifting Operations in Oklahoma City Field," *The Oil Weekly,* Vol. LXXXVII, No. 1 (September 13, 1937), 19.

Singleton, F. L. "Open 17 Pools on Gulf Coast; Deeper Pay Sands Located," *The Oil and Gas Journal,* Vol. XXXIV, No. 37 (January 30, 1936), 111.

Smiley, Thomas F. "Texas in Fight on Crude Price Ends," *The Oil and Gas Journal,* Vol. XXVIII, No. 36 (January 23, 1930), 33.

————. "Oil Scout Has Fewer Thrills But More Responsibility," *The Oil and Gas Journal,* Vol. XXXV, No. 42 (March 4, 1937), 16.

————. "Drilled in 1882, Kansas' Discovery Gas Well is Still Producing," *The Oil and Gas Journal,* Vol. XXX, No. 34 (January 7, 1932), 15.

————. "Danced by Light of First Kansas Gas," *The Oil and Gas Journal,* Vol. XXX, No. 44 (March 17, 1932), 17.

Sohn, J. Arthur. "Unitization vs. Competition," *The Oil Weekly,* Vol. LXXXIII, No. 2 (September 21, 1936), 22.

Spinney, W. A. "Outside Factors Hold Back Oklahoma," *The Oil and Gas Journal,* Vol. XXX, No. 37 (January 28, 1932), 64.

————. "Oklahoma's Flood of New Production," *The Oil and Gas Journal,* Vol. XXIX, No. 37 (January 29, 1931), 107.

Swindell, Floyd. "Study of Salt Water Problems," *The Oil Weekly,* Vol. LXXX, No. 6 (January 20, 1936), 66.

Taylor, Frank. "Pumping Unit," *The Oil Weekly,* Vol. LXXXVII, No. 10 (November 15, 1937), 23.

————. "Specialization of Equipment is Distinct Trend the Past Year," *The Oil Weekly,* Vol. LXXXVI, No. 1 (June 14, 1937), 125.

————. "Mid-Continent Water Flooding Survey," *The Oil Weekly,* Vol. LXXXVI, No. 2 (June 21, 1937), 56.

————. "Hugoton Gas Area Provided Kansas With One of Nation's Greatest Gas Reserves," *The Oil Weekly,* Vol. LXXXV, No. 8 (May 3, 1937), 56.

Thomas, A. E. "Oil and Its Relation to Banking," *The Oil and Gas Journal,* Vol. XXV, No. 40 (February 24, 1927), 32.

Bibliography

Triplett, Grady. "History of Arkansas," *The Oil Weekly,* Vol. LXXXIX, No. 3 (March 28, 1938), 68.

———. "They Do Come Back," *The Oil Weekly,* Vol. LXXXVIII, No. 6 (January 17, 1938), 28.

———. "Houston as Outlet for Mid-Continent," *The Oil and Gas Journal,* Vol. XXII, No. 15 (September 6, 1923), 56.

———. "History of North Louisiana," *The Oil Weekly,* Vol. LXXXIX, No. 3 (March 28, 1938), 92.

———. "History of East Texas," *The Oil Weekly,* Vol. LXXXIX, No. 3 (March 28, 1938), 131.

———. "Western Kansas History Dates Back to 1888, but First Commercial Well was in 1923," *The Oil Weekly,* Vol. LXXXV, No. 8 (May 3, 1937), 50.

Von Buelow, E. V. "Essential Points in Use in Geophysics," *The Oil and Gas Journal,* Vol. XXVIII, No. 33 (January 2, 1930), 34.

Williams, Neil. "Can Aerial Geology Locate Productive Oil and Gas Areas?" *The Oil and Gas Journal,* Vol. XXX, No. 35 (January 14, 1932), 11.

———. "New Practices Used in Pipe Conditioning to Combat Corrosion," *The Oil and Gas Journal,* Vol. XXXIV, No. 5 (June 20, 1935), 14.

———. "Gulf Coast Transportation Problems," *The Oil and Gas Journal,* Vol. XXVIII, No. 35 (January 16, 1930), 41.

———. "Keeping Control of Cratered Oil Well in Conroe Presents as Difficult Problems as Killing It," *The Oil and Gas Journal,* Vol. XXXII, No. 35 (January 18, 1934), 15.

———. "Position of President Roosevelt on Oil Placed Before I.P.A.A. Convention," *The Oil and Gas Journal,* Vol. XXXIV, No. 25 (November 7, 1935), 23.

———. "Martial Law Awaiting Briefs," *The Oil and Gas Journal,* Vol. XXX, No. 35 (January 14, 1932), 12.

———. "Martial Law Cases Before Federal Court," *The Oil and Gas Journal,* Vol. XXX, No. 34 (January 7, 1932), 13.

ARTICLES IN HOUSE ORGANS

Ames, C. B. "Petroleum and the Law," *The Texaco Star,* Vol. XVIII, No. 10 (November, 1931), 9.

Ashburn, Sam. "School Days in West Texas," *The Texaco Star,* Vol. XVIII, No. 6 (June-July, 1931), 28.

————. "Prosperity Comes to West Texas," *The Texaco Star,* Vol. XVI, No. 10 (December, 1929), 25.

————. "Tex Thornton—One-Man Fire Department," *The Texaco Star,* Vol. XVII, No. 1 (January, 1930), 13.

————. "Along the Pipe Line Trail," *The Texaco Star,* Vol. XVII, No. 4 (April, 1930), 23.

Bailey, A. S. "Our New West Texas Pipe Line," *The Texaco Star,* Vol. XVI, No. 7 (September, 1929), 1.

Bell, Willette N. "West Dallas Works—A History," *The Texaco Star,* Vol. XVII, No. 7 (July-August, 1930), 19.

Bignell, L. G. E. "New Compressed Air Unit for Pumping Oil Wells," *The Pure Oil News,* Vol. XV, No. 7 (December, 1932), 14.

"The Birth of Magnolia Changed the Oil Map of America," *The Magnolia Oil News,* Vol. XVI, No. 5 (April, 1931), 13.

Bonham, M. J. "Today's Picture of East Texas," *The Conoco Magazine,* Vol. III, No. 8 (May-June, 1932), 10.

Brumley, R. H. "A Famous Oklahoma Pool," *The Pure Oil News,* Vol. XI, No. 8 (January, 1929), 10.

Chamberlain, D. K. "Ardmore Refinery Has an Interesting History," *The Pure Oil News,* Vol. XI, No. 10 (March, 1929), 12.

DeRamus, Joseph S. "Chin Deep in Mud and Oil," *Rock Island Magazine,* Vol. XXII, No. 4 (April, 1927), 5.

Enger, Carl. "The Healdton Field," *The Pure Oil News,* Vol. X, No. 11 (April, 1928), 6.

Flynn, John T. "Bootleg Gasoline," *The Texaco Star,* Vol. XIX, No. 1 (January-February, 1932), 2.

Gaddis, Grace. "Home is Where the Hat is," *The Texaco Star,* Vol. XVIII, No. 5 (May, 1931), 14.

————. "Amusement in the 'Great Unfenced,'" *The Texaco Star,* Vol. XVII, No. 11 (December, 1930), 26.

Hurst, H. E. "Seminole Leads in Production of Natural Gasoline," *Rock Island Magazine,* Vol. XXIII, No. 2 (February, 1928), 16.

Bibliography

McLaughlin, R. B. "A Railway without Rails or Passengers," *The Texaco Star*, Vol. XVII, No. 11 (December, 1930), 9.

"Oil at the Dip of a Wooden Needle," *The Texaco Star*, Vol. XVIII, No. 2 (February, 1931), 13.

"Oklahoma and Oil-March Hand in Hand," *The Magnolia Oil News*, Vol. XVI, No. 5 (April, 1931), 55.

"Petroleum's Christmas Gift to the Southwest," *The Magnolia Oil News*, Vol. XVII, No. 1 (December, 1931), 3.

Sealy, F. C., and Miller, J. C. "East Texas, Bad Boy of the Oil Industry," *The Texaco Star*, Vol. XVIII, No. 8 (December, 1931), 3.

"Through Iowa via Pipe Line," *The Conoco Magazine*, Vol. II, No. 10 (June, 1931), 22.

"Times Do Change—Especially in Laredo," *The Rig and Reel Magazine*, Vol. IX, No. 5 (July, 1927), 10.

"The Van Unit," *The Pure Oil News*, Vol. XIII, No. 10 (March, 1931), 4.

Weaver, Gusta B. "Wildcat," *The Texaco Star*, Vol. XVIII, No. 3 (October, 1931), 25.

ARTICLES IN POPULAR MAGAZINES

Brown, Stonewall. "A Fortune in Oil—The Promoter Speaks," *The Atlantic Monthly*, Vol. CXLI, No. 1 (January, 1928), 96.

"Continental Oil," *Fortune*, Vol. XIX, No. 6 (June, 1939), 71.

Donoghue, Gerald. "Texas Banks Its Oil," *The Atlantic Monthly*, Vol. CLXIV, No. 3 (September, 1939), 370.

Liggett, Walter W. "Whoopee in Oklahoma," *Plain Talk*, Vol. XI, No. 6 (June, 1930), 641.

MacIntosh, P. J. R. "The Wonder Story of Texas Oil," *Bunker's Monthly*, Vol. II, No. 4 (October, 1928), 490.

"The Magic Knock of Fortune," *The Literary Digest*, Vol. XLVIII, No. 11 (March 14, 1914), 568.

"Monsieur Houdry's Invention," *Fortune*, Vol. XIX, No. 2 (February, 1939), 56.

Reed, Charles Leroy. "Oklahoma's Oil Field," *Sturm's Oklahoma Magazine*, Vol. IX, No. 2 (October, 1909), 68.

Flush Production

NEWSPAPERS AND NEWSPAPER ARTICLES

Files of the newspaper collection of the Oklahoma Historical Society, Oklahoma City, Oklahoma.

"First Shipment of Oil from Nickle Creek Test," *The Tulsa World,* Tulsa, Oklahoma, January 24, 1937.

Root, Tom. "Records Indicate Indians Need Help," *The Muskogee Phoenix,* Muskogee, Oklahoma, February 5, 1939.

Snyder, Bryan, Jr. "Oil History of Oklahoma," *The Daily Oklahoman,* Oklahoma City, Oklahoma, April 5–7, 1931.

Thompson, Lawrence. "After the Oil," *The Daily Oklahoman,* Oklahoma City, Oklahoma, January 15, 1939.

BOOKS

American Petroleum Institute. *Handbook for Speakers.* New York, 1928.

———. *Petroleum Facts and Figures* (sixth and seventh editions). New York, 1939, 1941.

Arnold, Ralph, and Kemnitzer, William J. *Petroleum in the United States and Possessions.* New York, 1931.

Ball, Max W. *This Fascinating Oil Business.* Indianapolis, 1940.

Ely, Northcutt. *Oil Conservation Through Interstate Agreement.* Washington, 1933.

House, Boyce. *Were You in Ranger?* Dallas, 1935.

Ise, John. *The United States Oil Policy.* New Haven, 1920.

Jones, John P. (Slim). *Ten Years in the Oil Fields.* El Dorado, Arkansas (c. 1926).

Kemnitzer, William J. *Rebirth of Monopoly.* New York, 1938.

Kulp, Victor E. *Cases on Oil and Gas.* St. Paul, 1924.

Levin, David D. *Done in Oil.* New York, 1941.

Logan, Leonard M. *The Stabilization of the Petroleum Industry.* Norman, 1930.

Marcosson, Isaac F. *The Black Golconda.* New York, 1924.

Mid-Continent Oil and Gas Association. *Handbook on Unitization of Oil Pools.* St. Louis, 1930.

The Petroleum Register (eighteenth edition). New York, 1937.

Pettengill, Samuel B. *Hot Oil, The Problem of Petroleum.* New York, 1936.

Bibliography

Petty, Edward. *Developments in the Petroleum Refining Industry as Related to Overproduction of Crude Oil*. Norman, 1931.

Richards, W. A. (compiler). *The Oklahoma Red Book*, II. Oklahoma City, 1912.

Shuman, Ronald. *The Petroleum Industry, An Economic Survey*. Norman, 1940.

Snider, L. C. *Petroleum and Natural Gas in Oklahoma*. Oklahoma City, 1913.

————. *Oil and Gas in the Mid-Continent Field*. Oklahoma City, 1920.

Stocking, George Ward. *The Oil Industry and the Competitive System, A Study in Waste*. New York, 1925.

Thornton, W. W. *The Law of Oil and Gas* (revised by Simeon S. Willis), VI. Cincinnati, 1932.

Warner, C. A. *Texas Oil and Gas Since 1543*. Houston, 1939.

MISCELLANEOUS

Alexander, M. R. (editor). *Oil and Gas Developments*, National Oil Scouts Association of America, *Yearbook*, VIII. Houston, 1938.

American Petroleum Institute. "Taxes Affecting Petroleum Industry in Oil Producing States" (Ms.). New York, January 1, 1939.

————. *The Story of an American Industry* (pamphlet). New York, 1935.

Barrow, Claude. Letters to the author, October 1, 1939, and April 4, 1941.

Beal, Elithe Hamilton. "Petroleum—Its Hazards" (Ms.), "Frontiers of Progress" series, University of Texas Radio Broadcasts, January 8, 1940.

————. "Petroleum—Its Quest" (Ms.), "Frontiers of Progress" series, University of Texas Radio Broadcasts, January 1, 1940.

Beaumont Chamber of Commerce. *Beaumont* (pamphlet). Beaumont, Texas, n.d.

241

Bradley, Charles Jefferson (editor). *Oil and Gas Developments,* National Oil Scouts Association of America, *Yearbook,* IX. Houston, 1939.

Cole, William P., Jr. "Oil from the Standpoint of National Legislation" (Ms.), address before the Tenth Annual Meeting of the Independent Petroleum Association of America, Fort Worth, October 20, 1939.

————. Address before the General Session at the Twentieth Annual Meeting of the American Petroleum Institute (Ms.), Chicago, November 15, 1939.

Giddens, Paul H. Letter to the author, April 7, 1941.

Mapes, Clarel B. "A Review of the Petroleum Industry in Oklahoma," *Annual Report,* Mid-Continent Oil and Gas Association, 38. Tulsa, 1929.

Marland, E. W. Letter to the author, October 21, 1939.

"Natural Gas—Discovered" (Ms.), "Frontiers of Progress" series, University of Texas Radio Broadcasts, February 5, 1940.

"Natural Gas—Man's Secret" (Ms.), "Frontiers of Progress" series, University of Texas Radio Broadcasts, February 12, 1940.

Oil Well Supply Company, Ltd. *Illustrated Catalog.* New York, 1884, 1892.

Patchett, Glenn. "The Cushing Oil Field" (Ms.), Mid-Continent Oil and Gas Association, n. d.

Phillips, Leon C. Address before the General Session of the Twentieth Annual Meeting of the American Petroleum Institute (Ms.), Chicago, November 15, 1939.

Pogue, Joseph E. *A Design for More Effective Proration,* reprint of address before the American Institute of Mining and Metallurgical Engineers, February, 1939.

243

Burkburnett: 42, 51, 178; Schmocker No. 1 at, 45; Fowler well and boom at, 55f.; stock selling at, 134f.; rents at, 160; oil price at, 181; flush production at, 181f.; first Texas proration at, 182

Burrton Pool: discovery of, 103f.

Burton, W. M.: cracking process of, 124

Butane: 148; in refining, 124; in geochemistry, 127

Caddo Pool: 46, 219; first gas at, 46f.; marine wells at, 103

Calcasieu River: 7

Camden Pool: discovery of, 106

Carbon black: importance of, in Panhandle, 64f.; made in Louisiana, 78; development of industry, 149ff.

Casinghead: *see* Natural gasoline

Cayuga Pool: 94; discovery of, 96

Cedar Point Pool: 94

Chalk Pool: 219

Chanute: oil at, in 1899, 16; in 1903, 40

Chelsea: 12, 23

Chemistry: in exploring, 127

Cherokee: *see* Indians

Choate, George: Conroe study of, 95

Choctaw: *see* Indians

Cisco: in Ranger boom, 54

Civil War: effects of, 8f.

Cleveland Pool: in Oklahoma, 24f.; in Texas, 94

Cole, William P., Jr.: Congressman, bill for Federal regulation by, 200f.

Collins, Ray: umpire of Seminole, 71f., 184f.

Conflict of major and minor companies: 84ff., 187f.; in tariff dispute, 85f.

Connally Act: 99, 112, 195; administration of, 92; passed by Congress, 195

Conroe Pool: 94, 219; discovery and development of, 95f.; whipstock used at, 118

Conservation: (*see also* Proration, Regulation, Waste) in Kansas in 1917, 80; in East Texas spacing, 93; Arkansas law of, 107; as purpose of Interstate Oil Compact,

113; effort to limit Texas and Oklahoma gas for, 145; Kansas, Texas, Oklahoma beginnings of, 172f.; as affecting Texas gas in 1935, 176; Federal Oil Conservation Board, 184f.; conclusions as result of restricting, 186; purpose of, 187; use of term, 188; in development of compact, 195ff.; in Cole bill, 200f.

Cook, Dr. Frederick A.: convicted in stock selling, 137

Cook, Walter E.: discovers Zwolle Pool, 77

Corpus Christi: as refining center, 97; exporting at, 158

Corsicana: 152; discovery of oil at, 15f.; pipe line and refinery at, 15; importance of, 16; gas supplied to, 140; law resulting at, 172

Cotton Valley Pool: 74; discovery of, 76

Cox, S. E. J.: convicted in stock selling, 137

Cracking process: *see* Burton

Creek: *see* Indians

Creole Pool: 101; discovery of, 102

Crichton Pool: 46; discovery of, 48

Criminals: in oil towns, 162f.; in Wirt (Ragtown) 35; kidnapping, 209f.

Cromwell Pool: 67; ten producing zones at, 70

Cudahy, Michael: oil explorations of, 14

Cullinan, J. S.: Corsicana interests of, 15

Cushing Pool: 23, 45, 126, 131, 155, 169, 180, 181, 208, 218; discovery of, 30ff.; peak of, 32, 34; waste of gas at, 32, 144; oil storage at, 33; casinghead gas plants at, 48; Shamrock extension of, 67; stripper stage of, 111

Daisy Bradford No. 3: discovery of East Texas Pool at, 65f., 188

Delano, Frederick A.: as Red River receiver, 174

Desdemona Pool: 206, 207; discovery of, 54f.

DeSoto Pool: 46; discovery of, 47

Disney, Wesley: Congressman, oil control bill by, 194

Index

Doherty, Henry L.: Federal control urged by, 193; unit plan proposed by, 199
Drilling: significance of, in Blackwell discovery, 40; deep well, of 1908, 41; Hughes bit aids in, 44; in Burkburnett, 56; effects of World War on, 58; Big Lake depth of, 61; on highway barred, 63; in East Texas, 67, 91, 95; Garber effects on, 68; cost of, at Oklahoma City, 73; at Homer, 75; coastal difficulties in, 76; of pepperbox at Kilgore, 89 ff.; of directional hole at Conroe, 96; trouble in Edwards Plateau, 97; in Permian Basin, 98; in Rodessa, 99; marine, 101 f.; depth of, on Louisiana coast, 102; in deeper Kansas sands, 103; depth of, at Schuler, 107; in Oklahoma City extension, 109 f.; at Fox Pool and Binger wildcat, 111; developments in, 116 ff.; use of core in, 126 f.; under Rule 37, 188 f.; 10,000-foot wells, 216; costs of, 1940, 217 f.
Drumright: in Shaffer County movement, 32

Earlsboro: 70, 219; boom and bankruptcy of, 167
East Texas: 51, 86, 194, 206, 218; discovery of, 65 ff.; development of, 87 ff.; objects to Rodessa, 99; effect on price, 108; quality of oil from, 125; pipe lines at, 157; in Madison trial, 177 f.; effect of Rule 37 in, 188 f.
Eastland: in Ranger boom area, 54
Education: influenced by oil, 160 f.; support for, 168
Edwards Plateau: 97
El Dorado Pool: 183; discovery of, 78 f.
Eldorado Pool: 126, 219; growth of, 42; Trapshooters' well, 80
Electra Pool: 42, 55, 219; discovery of, 44 f.; deeper drilling at, 51
Exports: from Texas in 1904, 43; Galveston storage for, 59; from Texas in 1929, 65; from Corpus Christi, 97; from Gulf ports, 157 f.

Fairbanks Pool: 94

Fawcett, Hiram W.: wells drilled at Atoka and Tahlequah by, 12
Federal Oil Conservation Board: creation of and inquiry by, 184 f.
Federal Trade Commission: booklet by, 185; Interstate Oil Compact renewal urged by, 196
Fire: danger of, at Oklahoma City, 73; in Caddo Parish, 76; in East Texas, 90; fought with whipstocks, 118; of gas, 143; at Ardmore, 147
First World War: 181, 201; effect of, on prices, 48, 74; and Federal control, 50; effect of, at Ranger, 52; hampers drilling, 58; consequences of, 83; effect of, on stock selling, 131; and use of helium, 149; effect of, on pipe lines, 156 f.
Fitts Pool: discovery of, 110
Fort Worth: mecca for promoters at, 135 ff.; helium plant at, 149
Foster, Edwin B.: in 1896, Osage reservation leased by, 14
Fowler, S. L.: opens Burkburnett Pool, 55 f.
Franklin, Wirt: co-discoverer of Healdton, 34; town named for, 35; leads Independent Petroleum Association of America, 187 f.
Fuel from oil: first tried in locomotive at Corsicana, 16; use of in 1908, 44; for sugar refineries, 46; for ships, 84

Galey, John H.: see Guffey and Galey
Galveston: 170; in exporting, 59
Garber Pool: discovery and significance, 67 f.
Gas, Natural: in early Kansas wells, 9 f.; at Shreveport, 9 f.; in early Texas wells, 10; transporting from Oklahoma forbidden, 28, 141 f.; value of, in Oklahoma, 29; Cushing waste of, 32; 1904 Kansas consumption of, 41; Laredo supplied with, 44; holding of, in ground to aid oil flow, 63; in Arkansas in 1920, 78; in New Mexico, 82; in East Texas, 91; pressure of, in Texas, 97; Rodessa, waste of, 99; Hugoton development of, 104; in New Mexico in 1930, 105; mud

245

Flush Production

used to save, 120; in refining, 124; growth of, industry, 139 ff.; as nuisance, 141; Oklahoma law on, enjoined, 142; Oklahoma and Texas laws to save, 145; in carbon black, 149 ff.; suggested Panhandle line for, 155; first Texas law on, 172; 1935 Texas conservation act on, 176

Gasoline: high Cushing grade of, 32 f.; economy urged for, 84; from East Texas, 88, 91; improved by polymerization, 124; pipeline for, 158; in Madison trial, 177; amount of, produced in Mid-Continent, 197; taxes on, 218 f.

Geological Survey: organized in Kansas, 8; United States surveys of Osage, 68; organization of, in Oklahoma, 125; of United States, 185

Geology: 116; companies departments of, 32; Springer Pool result of, 34; aids Rodessa extension, 99; implications of, at Fox Pool and Binger wildcat, 111; development of, 125 f.; college and school study of, 162; explains graveyard oil theory, 213 f.

Geophysics: proved value of, 61; on Gulf Coast, 63; in Louisiana, 78; in Kansas, 81; in New Mexico, 82; Rodessa extension aided by, 99; in Kansas, 103; development of, 126 f.

Glenn Pool: 23, 142, 154, 155, 169, 218; discovery and growth of, 25 f.; 1907 peak of, 27; pipe lines to, 26 f.; oil from, to Baton Rouge, 47; natural gasoline at, 120; school at, 161

Goose Creek Pool: 51; discovery of, 44; revival of, 58

Gordon, W. K.: discovers Ranger Pool, 52 f.

Gorham Pool: 80

Gould, Charles N.: Oklahoma production forecast by, 31; on Panhandle drilling, 58; Oklahoma Geological Survey organized by, 125

Graham, Jack: 8

Great Lakes Pipe Line: to move gasoline, 158

Guffey, J. M. and Galey, John H.: in Kansas, 13

Gulf Coast: Spindletop on, 16 ff.; output of, as fuel, 45; geophysics on, 61, 63, 126; drilling difficulties on, 76; Conroe on, 95; reserves of, 97; berths for tankers on, 98; Louisiana pools on, 102; low viscosity of oil from, 125; long pipe lines to, 154; refining on, 217

Gulf Coast Products Association: aids Texas proration, 182 f.

Gulf Oil Corporation: 170; Glenn pipe line of, 27; founding of, 138; pipe line to coast, 154

Hamon, Jake L.: builds railroad from Ardmore, 35; town named for, 135; Texas railroad of, 165

Haskell, Charles N.: Governor, stops pipe line crew, 142; wants pipe line, 155

Haynesville Pool: 74; discovery of, 76

Healdton Pool: 23, 67, 131, 155, 162, 181, 219; Palmer prospects at, 12; development of, 34 ff.; Magnolia pipe line to, 35; as poor man's pool, 36; difficulties with Magnolia at, 36 f.; oil prices at, 37 f.

Helium: discovery and extraction of, 148 f.

Hendrick Pool: 219; discovery of, 62; record of, 64; proration asked for, 186

Heydrick, Jesse A.: 204; Red Fork discovery of, 23

Higgens, Patillo: drills at Spindletop, 16; oil company of, 17

Hobbs Pool: 86, 219; discovery of, 82; 1934 yield of, 105; proration asked for, 186

Hogshooter Gas Pool: discovery and development, 142 f.

"Hot" oil: in East Texas, 89 ff., 192; Connally Act, 92

Homer Pool: 74; discovery of, 75 f.

Houston: 170; stock selling at, 129; exporting at, 157

Hughes, H. R.: bit devised by, 44

Hugoton Gas Pool: 80; development of, 104; by 1933, 146

Hull Pool: 51, discovery of, 58

Index

Humble Oil and Refining Company: at Desdemona, 55; founding of, 138

Humble Pool: 219; discovery of, 43

Humphreys, A. E.: discovers Mexia, 60

Hydrogenation: 124

Ickes, Harold L.: 91 f., 177, 191, 194

Illinois: established market upset by, 113; idle Ranger pipe lines moved to, 157; refiners of southwest compete with, 158

Independence: gas and oil at, 11; oiling street car tracks at, 12; gas piped to, 140

Independent Petroleum Association of America: origin of, 187 f.; in East Texas dispute, 191; speech before, 193

Indians: 210 ff.; leases of, hindered, 10; enterprises of Cherokees and Choctaws, 12; allotments of, 14, 23; lease to Heydrick and Wick, 23; Cushing wealth of Creeks, 31; Navajo lease, 81; 1940 status of Five Tribes, 111; affected by security selling, 130; leases of, 144, 153; effect of oil wealth on, 166; Crazy Snake war, 204 f.; arbitrary allotments of, 205; guardianship cases of, 211

Indian Territory: see Oklahoma

Indian Territory Illuminating Oil Company: lease of Osage Reservation to, 27; lease terminated, 39; discovery at Oklahoma City by, 72

International Petroleum Exposition: proposed and held, 70

Interstate Commerce Commission: gains authority over pipe lines, 155 f.

Interstate Oil Compact: Colorado Springs meeting of, 85 f.; Louisiana not a member of, 102; organization of Interstate Oil Compact Commission, 112 f., 192 f.; meetings and organization, 195 f.; opinions regarding, 197

Iola: 139; deep well near, 41

Iowa Park Pool: discovery of, 45

Jal Pool: discovery of, 82; importance of, 105

Jennings Pool: 46; effects of Spindletop on, 20; screen used at, 46

Johnson, Roy: co-discoverer of Healdton, 34

Joiner, C. M. ("Dad"): 188; discovers East Texas Pool, 65 f.

Kansas: 114, 123, 126, 150, 152, 157, 160, 179, 186, 187, 192, 199, 217; geological survey of, formed, 8; early gas wells, 9 ff.; early oil in, 12 f.; first conservation law of, 13; 1900 production value in, 16; 1901–15 developments in, 40 f.; pipe line organized in, 40; value of oil and gas in, 41; 1904 extent of industry, 41; pipe line to Indiana from, 41; Bolton discovered in, 40 f.; Eldorado and Augusta discovered in, 41 f.; 1915–30 developments in, 80 ff.; oil employment in, 81; 1930–40 growth of industry in, 103 f.; gas in, 139 ff.; opposition to Standard in, 153 f.; first oil law in, 172 f.; stringent tax fought in, 173 f.; first proration in, 186

Kansas Public Service Commission: given authority over industry, 103

Kansas State Geological Survey: organized, 8; Miami county report by, 9

Kavanaugh, B. T.: Oklahoma and Texas oil predicted by, 8

K-M-A (Kemp-Munger-Allen): 51, 94; discovery of, 57; deep wells at, 95

Kerosene: chief early petroleum product, 11, 123; law regarding, 172

Kilgore: discovery well near, 66; pepperbox drilling at, 89

Lake Charles: early oil near, 7, 11; Spindletop effect on, 20

Lake Hermitage Pool: 101

Lake Washington Pool: 101

Landon, Alfred: Governor of Kansas, 169

Laredo: gas discovery at, 44; oil discovery at, 59

Legend of discovery: 202 f.

Lisbon Pool: 101; discovery of, 102

Lockport Pool: 74; discovery of, 76 142

247

dian explorations in, 12; Chelsea discovery in, 12; developments by 1897 in, 14; 1900 production in, 23; output in 1904, 25; statehood of, 27; 1907 production in, 27; Indian guardianships in, 28; gas exportation barred by, 28; developments of 1915–30 in, 67 ff.; oil employment in, 73; oil taxes in, 73, 219; 1930–40 developments in, 108 ff.; gas industry in, 140 ff.; effort to limit gas flow in, 145; opposition to Standard Oil Company in, 154 f.; common carrier law in, 173; in Red River conflict, 174 f.; administration of industry in, 178; economic waste illegal in, 181; demand estimates wanted in, 193

Oklahoma City Pool: 67, 86; discovery of, 72 f.; wild well in, 73; development of, 108 f.; quality of oil, 125; royalty share sales at, 138

Oklahoma Corporation Commission: Cushing wells limited by, 33; in Healdton controversy, 37 f.; conservation of oil in storage by, 39; in restricting Seminole, 71 f.; allocates Oklahoma City Pool, 108; authority over gas given to, 145; authority of, discussed, 173; in administrative law, 178 f.; rules of, nullified, 181; Hewitt Pool orders of, 183; Ray Collins sanctioned by, 184 f.

Okmulgee: many small pools near, 68

Orange Pool: 51, 206; discovery of, 60

Ordovician: Kay County well in, 40; (*see also* Blackwell)

Osage: 212 f.; reservation of, leased, 14; pipe line on lands of, 25; roll of, closed, 27; lease of, renewed, 27; Indian Territory Illuminating Oil Company lease of, ended, 39, 68; pools in county of, 69; oil receipts of between 1912 and 1939, 111; boundary dispute of, 175; quarterly payments to, 212

Oxford Pool: discovery of, 104

Palmer, ————: Healdton oil

found by, 12; discovery of, studied, 34

Panhandle Pool: 51; discovery of, 58; oil in Carson, Potter, Hutchinson counties, 59 f.; value of gas from, 64; leads world in gas, 145 ff.

Paola: 139; exploration at, 9; gas industry center at, 10 f., 13

Paraffin: base of Rodessa oil, 100; problem of, 120, 125

Pennsylvania: 152, oil tools from, 10, 22; oil men from, 11, 13; water flooding begun in, 122 f.

Permian Basin: 105, 113; New Mexico explorations in, 82; Texas pools in, 98

Petrolia: 42; Wichita Oil Company at, 43; helium extracted at, 149

Phillips Petroleum Company: gasoline pipe line of, 158

Pierce Junction Pool: 51; discovery of, 60

Pine Island Pool: 74; over production at, 74 f.

Pine Prairie Pool: 46; discovery of, 47

Pipe Lines: first, in Texas, 12; to Neodesha, 25; to Whiting, Indiana, 26, 41; Gulf Oil Corporation and The Texas Company, to Glenn Pool, 27; plan as common carriers, 29; from Glenn Pool to Baton Rouge, 29; Navy investigates, from Cushing, 32; from Healdton to Texas, 35; Prairie Oil and Gas Company organized, 40; to Sour Lake, 42; in Texas in 1905, 43; three in Louisiana in 1910, 47; to Burkburnett, 57; in Texas in 1919, 59; to Big Lake, 61; gas from Panhandle by, 61; absence of, at Yates, 62; at Homer, 76; Kansas development delayed for, 81; in New Mexico, 82; in East Texas, 88 ff.; empty East Texas tanks, 93; to Beaumont-Port Arthur, 97 f; near Rodessa, 99; extended in Kansas, 104; New Mexico oil and gas through, 105; aided by aerial photographs, 126; Lone Star Gas Company formed, 142; for gas, 145 f.; growth of, 152 ff.; ditching machines for, 157; Kansas and Oklahoma made com-

mon carriers of, 173; output limited to capacity of, 181; conclusions from limiting to capacity of, 186; Oklahoma to New York, 217
Polymerization: 124
Port Arthur: refineries at, 21, 97f., 152f., 217
Powell Pool: 42, 219
Prairie Oil and Gas Company: Osage pipe line of, 25; to Cushing, 31; organized, first pipe line laid, 40; to Kansas City and Whiting, Indiana, 41; Kansas opposition to, 153ff.; protests Federal control, 156
Price of oil and gas: at Spindletop, 19; at Glenn, 25, 27; at Cushing, 32f.; at Healdton, 37f.; 1905–11, in Kansas, 41; in Texas, 42ff.; in Louisiana in 1907, 47; in general, 53; of Tonkawa oil, 70; at Seminole, 70; in 1917, 83; 1921 peak of, 84; effect of Seminole and Yates on, 85; decline of, in East Texas, 88f.; of East Texas gasoline in 1938, 94; 1930 price in Arkansas, 106; effect on development, 108; attempt to fix, in Oklahoma, 181; drops at Burkburnett, 181; as purpose of proration, 187; drops in East Texas, 190f.; effect of East Texas on, 192; shutdown follows cut in, 197
Production: cumulative for Gulf-Southwest and comparisons, 216; for thirty greatest pools in Gulf-Southwest, 218f.
Promotion of oil companies: at Ranger, 55ff.; in 1919, 84
Propane: 148, in refining, 124; in geochemistry, 127
Proration: Mexia wells pinched for, 60; urged in Texas, 59nl.; introduced at Yates, 62; effect of, on East Texas, 67; at Seminole, 71f.; at Oklahoma City, 73; arranged in New Mexico, 82; urged by industry, 85f.; East Texas difficulties in, 87ff.; in West Texas, 97; at Rodessa, 100; in Kansas in 1931, 103; effect of on New Mexico, 105; Arkansas difficulties and rules of, 106f.; martial law in Oklahoma, 108; Yates results of, 122;

attempt of, in Texas gas, 176; defined, 181; first, in Texas, 182; at Yates and Seminole, 184; requests for, 186; first, in Kansas, 186; purpose of, 187; value seen in, 188; Rule 37 of, 188f.; fixing allowables for, 189f.; basic features of, 194; arguments regarding, 197ff.
Public Service Commission of Kansas: 103
Pump: windmills used to, 80, 96; necessary as pressure falls, 94; New Mexico problem of, 106; introduced at Oklahoma City, 108, 110; at Glenn Pool, 120; electric rotary, 121f.; older men at stations for, 160
Pure Oil Company: Van unit project operated by, 65

Railroad: from Ardmore, 35; freight at Borger, 65; fuel used by, 83; near Rodessa, 99; promotion of, 135; in oil area, 165
Rainbow Bend Pool: 80
Ranger Pool: 161, 162, 178, 205, 207; discovery and boom of, 51ff; stock selling at, 135ff.; prediction on, 136; pipe lines to, 157; freight at, 165
Rattlesnake Dome Pool: 82
Recycling: by acid and water in Kansas, 103; methods of, 121f.
Red Fork: 153, 169; boom at, 23f.; Clinton and Bland, 24nl.; speculation stimulated by, 130, 204
Red River: 59; "Great Raft" of, 77; conflict of Oklahoma and Texas over, 174f.
Reeser, E. B.: President of American Petroleum Institute, names committees, 186f.
Refineries: at Neodesha, Sour Lake, Corsicana, 15f.; at Port Arthur, 21; in Wichita County, Texas, 58; 1930 employees in Texas at, 65; 1919 in Louisiana, 75, 1930 in Louisiana, 78; 1931 condition of, 87; East Texas activities of, 88ff.; in Beaumont–Port Arthur area, 98; in New Mexico, 105; changes in, 116, 123f.; on Texas Gulf Coast, 157f., 217; forced to close

Index

in East Texas, 192; 1940 rank of Texas, 216f.; value of products, 217

Regulation of industry: (*see also* Proration) co-operation legalized in New Mexico, 82; in piping gas from Oklahoma, 141; pipe lines made common carriers in Oklahoma, 154f.; in Texas, 155; on Sundays in Arkansas, 162; legal aspects of, 172ff.; development of proration, 181ff.; proposals for, 186f.; East Texas trouble, in 188ff.; by interstate agreement, 192f.; different plans for, 193f.; arguments about, 197ff.; Cole bill for, 200f.

Religion: affected by oil, 162

Reserves of oil: on Gulf Coast, 97; at Rodessa, 100; in Louisiana, 102; in Kansas, 104; decline of, in Oklahoma, 112; position of Gulf Coast in, 113; in Permian Basin, 113; rank of southwestern states in, 114f.

Ritz-Canton Pool: 80; proration of, 81; proration asked at, 186

Roanoke Pool: 101

Rodessa Pool: 74, 94, 101f.; 179, 195, 219; Louisiana gas at, 77; Texas and Arkansas extension of, 98ff.; dissipation of, in Arkansas, 106

Rotary drilling: developed at Corsicana, 16; Hughes bit, 44; at Spindletop, 117; variety in, 119

Rowe, W. H.: discovers Homer Pool, 75

Royalties: Osage division of, 27; to Five Tribes, 28; increase of, to Osages, 39; sold in shares at Ranger, 55; of Osage leases, 68f.; sale of, at Seminole, 70; sale of fractions of, 138

Salt Dome: at Spindletop, 20; studied through geophysics, 61, 126

Salt Water: (*see also* Water) in East Texas, 93

Santa Rita Well: 61

Saratoga Pool: pipe line to, 43; no decline at, 44

Schuler Pool: discovery of, 107

Scouts: change plan of work, 71

Schrock, Dr. E. P.: develops carbon black method, 150

Seepages: of oil and gas, 7f., 125

Seismograph: (*see also* Geophysics) found practical, 61f.

Seminole Pool: 67, 86, 162, 167, 183, 219; discovery and growth of, 70ff.; effect on price, 85; freight at 165; orders to limit, 184

Shaffer County: campaign to organize, 32f.

Shreveport: 9, 140

Sinclair, Harry F.: 164

Slick, Thomas B.: discovers Cushing Pool, 30

Smackover Pool: 183, 218; discovery and development of, 79; as stripper area, 107; flush production of, 183

Smith, Lon: Texas Railroad Commission member, denounces Interstate Oil Compact, 196

Sneed, Earl: starts International Petroleum Exposition, 70

Sour Lake Pool: 42f.; refinery at, 15

Spindletop Pool: 7, 42, 113, 126, 129f., 219; work by Higgins at, 16f.; work by Lucas at, 17f.; work of Guffey and Galey at, 17; pipe line by T. Mellon and Sons at, 18; use of muddy water at, 17; output of, 18f., 63; fire at, 18; tank cars from, 18; 1925 revival of, 62f.; rotary bit at, 117

Splendora Pool: 94

Springer Pool: result of geological study, 34

Standard Oil Company: (*see also* Prairie Oil and Gas Company) Corsicana refinery of, 15; Spindletop oil refused by, 18; pipe line of, to Whiting, Indiana, 26; cracking and hydrogenation patents of, 124; subsidiary of, moves crude, 152f;. opposition to, 153f.; Baton Rouge pipe line of, 154

Sterling, Ross: Governor of Texas, 169; declares martial law, 88, 19f.

Stock selling: at Spindletop, 19f.; at Ranger, 51ff.; at Desdemona, 55; at Wichita Falls, 57; in 1919,

Flush Production

84; on the fraudulent fringe, 129 ff.
Storage of oil: at Glenn Pool, 28; at Cushing, 33; Oklahoma Corporation Commission rules on, 39; at Desdemona, 59; at Mexia, 60; in West Texas, 64; at Homer, 76; at Smackover, 79; in 1917, 83; by large companies, 85; in East Texas, 87 ff., 90
Strake, George W.: discovers Conroe Pool, 95
Stripper wells: in Kansas in 1940, 103; in Arkansas, 106; at Smackover, 107 f.; not closed in Oklahoma, 108; at Cushing, 111
Sulphur: 125; at Healdton, 36; in Panhandle gas, 64, 146; in Kansas oil, 104; eliminated by hydrogenation, 124 f.

Tariff on oil: outcome of Colorado Springs meeting, 86; enacted, 188
Taxes: in Oklahoma, 73, in Gulf-Southwest, 168 f.; fought in Kansas, 173 f.; list of, 218 f.
Teagle, Walter C.: asks co-operation, 184
Texas: 114, 123, 129, 157, 160, 183, 186, 187, 192, 195, 199, 216; probable first oil well in, 8; first pipeline in, 12; oil near San Antonio, 13; first permanent refinery in, 15 f.; first conservation law of, 16; 1901–15 developments in, 42 ff.; 1915–30 growth of industry in, 50 ff.; 1930 employment of industry in, 65; oil confiscated by, 92; 1940 employment in, 98; 1940 position of, 101; speculative stock selling in, 132 ff.; gas in, 139 ff.; effort to limit gas in, 145; carbon black leadership of, 150; pipe line laws passed in, 155; first gas law in, 172; Red River conflict, 174 f.; administration of industry in, 178; first proration in, 182; efforts to control East Texas, 188 f.; refining industry led by, 216 f.
Texas Independent Refiners Association: 90 f.
Texas and Pacific Coal Company: in discovery of Ranger, 51 ff.
Texas Railroad Commission: 175,

181 f.; authority over oil given to, 59 n l.; proration of Yates by, 62; and East Texas discovery, 67; East Texas rules by, 87 ff.; allowables for East Texas of, 89; Sunday shutdown in East Texas by, 93; Rodessa allowables by, 100; United States Supreme Court overrules, 147; pipe line control given to, 155; gas control given to, 176; in administrative law, 178 f.; Burkburnett proration asked of, 182; oil men asked to assist by, 182; Yates proration asked of, 184; operations of, 188 f.; authority sustained, 189; East Texas difficulties of, 190 ff.
The Texas Company: 170; Glenn Pool pipe line of, 27; founded at Spindletop, 138; pipe line to Gulf of, 154
The University of Texas: 161; allotment of land to, 10 n 2.; Big Lake discovery, 61
Thomas, Elmer: Senator, bill of, 194
Tomball Pool: 94
Tonkawa Pool: 67, 219; discovery and development of, 69 f.
Transportation: (see also Pipe Lines, Railroad) 152; in the oil region, 164 f.
Troy Pool: discovery of, 106
Tulsa: 70, 143, 144, 168; benefits from Glenn Pool, 25 f.; sizes of, in 1922, 70; supplied with gas, 140; Commercial Club of, in gas argument, 141; pipe lines to, 153; banking at, 164; created by oil, 169 f.

United States Bureau of Corporations: Healdton investigated by, 37
United States Bureau of Mines: in 1918 reserves estimated by, 53; estimate by, 94; Louisiana avoids estimates of, 102; mud-laden fluid demonstrated by, 120, 144 f.; demand estimated by, 193, 196
United States Department of the Interior: hinders Indian land leasing, 10; approves Indian leases, 24; removes Indian restrictions, 27; Indian land drilling rules by,

252

FLUSH PRODUCTION

HAS BEEN COMPOSED ON THE LINOTYPE

IN OLD STYLE NUMBER SEVEN

AND PRINTED UPON

ANTIQUE WOVE

PAPER

UNIVERSITY OF OKLAHOMA PRESS

NORMAN

Date Due

		PRINTED IN U. S. A.	